Spelling

GRADE TWO

ACSI Spelling

Acknowledgements

The ACSI Spelling Series is the product of a remarkable team of Christian educators.

Editorial Team

Dr. Sharon Berry—Managing Editor, Dr. Barry Morris—Content Editor, and Dr. Ollie Gibbs—Project Director

Author Team

Mrs. Sharon Bird, Mrs. Cathy Guy, Mrs. Eunice Harris, Miss Linda Miller, Mrs. Nancy Wetsel, and Mrs. Connie Williams

Project Consultants

Dr. Barbara Bode, Dr. Richard Edlin, Dr. Omer Bonenberger, Dr. Linda Goodson, Dr. Alex Lackey, Mrs. Ruth McBride, Dr. Connie Pearson, Mrs. Patti Rahn, Dr. Milton Uecker, and Dr. Ray White

To enable Christian educators and schools worldwide to effectively prepare students for life

Publishing is a function of the Academic Affairs Department of ACSI. As an organization, ACSI is committed to the ministry of Christian school education, to enable Christian educators and schools worldwide to effectively prepare students for life. As a publisher of books, textbooks, and other resources, ASCI endeavors to produce biblically sound materials that reflect Christian scholarship and stewardship, and that address the identified needs of Christian schools around the world.

For additional information, write ACSI, Academic Affairs Department, PO Box 35097, Colorado Springs, CO 80935-3509.

Printed in the United States of America

ACSI Elementary Spelling—Grade Two Student Edition
ISBN 1-58331-156-4 **Catalog #** 7409

Association of Christian Schools International
PO Box 35097 • Colorado Springs, CO • 80935-3509
Order Department: 800/367-0798 • Website: http://www.acsi.org

ACSI SPELLING

Contents • Grade Two

and

as

listen

set

ten

legs

sad

met

kitten

seven

pencil

mix-up

LESSON 1 Target: Short vowels **e**, **a**, and **i**

A **Missing Vowels.** Put in the missing vowels in your list words.

__s	k__tt__n
m__t	s__v__n
p__nc__l	s__d
l__gs	__nd
s__t	l__st__n
t__n	m__x-__p

Write your Home Base Words. Circle the vowels.

B **Match-Up.** Match the words with their shapes. Write the word in its box.

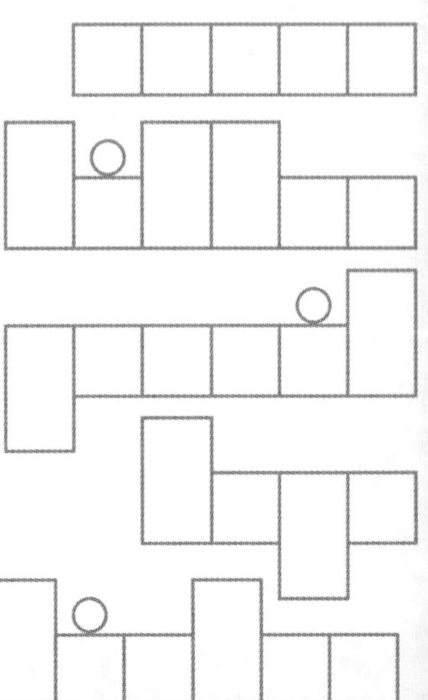

C **Mix–Up.** Mix–up is a fun word. It is two small words put together with a line called a hyphen. Write mix–up two times.

1. ____________________

2. ____________________

D **A Mixed–Up Day.** One day Amy had a mix-up with her clothes. She put her shoes on her hands. She put her socks on her head. She put her hat on her feet. Draw a picture of confused Amy.

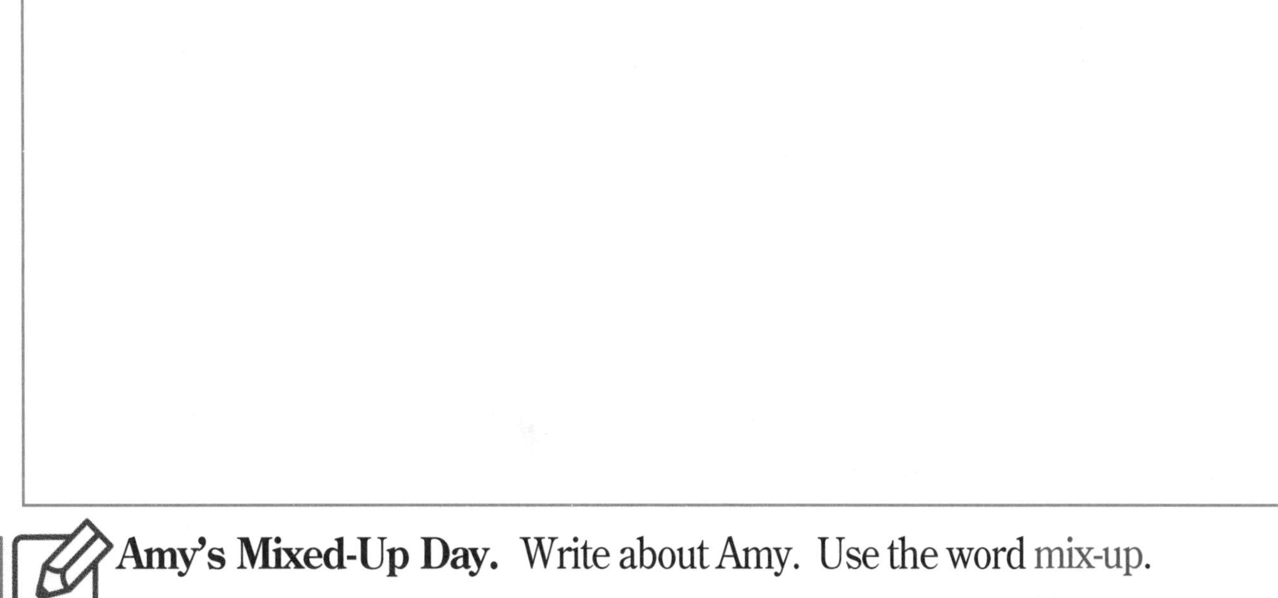

E **Amy's Mixed-Up Day.** Write about Amy. Use the word mix-up.

F **Words in Pictures.** It is fun to make words into shape pictures. See the shape pictures for pencil and seven.

Pencil

s e v e n

Make shape pictures for legs, kitten, and sad.

G **Seven.** The number seven is a very important number in the Bible. It is used many times. Psalm 119:164 says, "Seven times a day I praise you." Write seven things you can praise God for today. Share your list with two friends. See what they wrote.

H **Word Sets.** Met and set are rhyming words. Write a list word to rhyme with these words.

pegs ______	get ______
sand ______	dad ______
pen ______	has ______

☐ Have you put your Home Base Words in the Glossary? Color the box red if you have.

and
as
listen
set
ten
legs
sad
met
kitten
seven
pencil
mix–up

I **Friends.** Billy, Janie, Mike, Beth, Tony and Maria are friends from the neighborhood. You will share many adventures with them through the year. Today they are putting together a new robot named Robbie. Write a story about the picture.

J **Robbie Robot.** Help put Robbie together by drawing his legs.

of*
but
if
until
rabbit
six
wagon
Monday
win
September*
wisdom
Gospel

LESSON 2 Target: Short vowel sounds **u**, **o**, and **i**

A **Letters and Colors.** Write your spelling words on the house. Circle all the u's with red. Circle all the o's with blue. Circle all the i's with green.

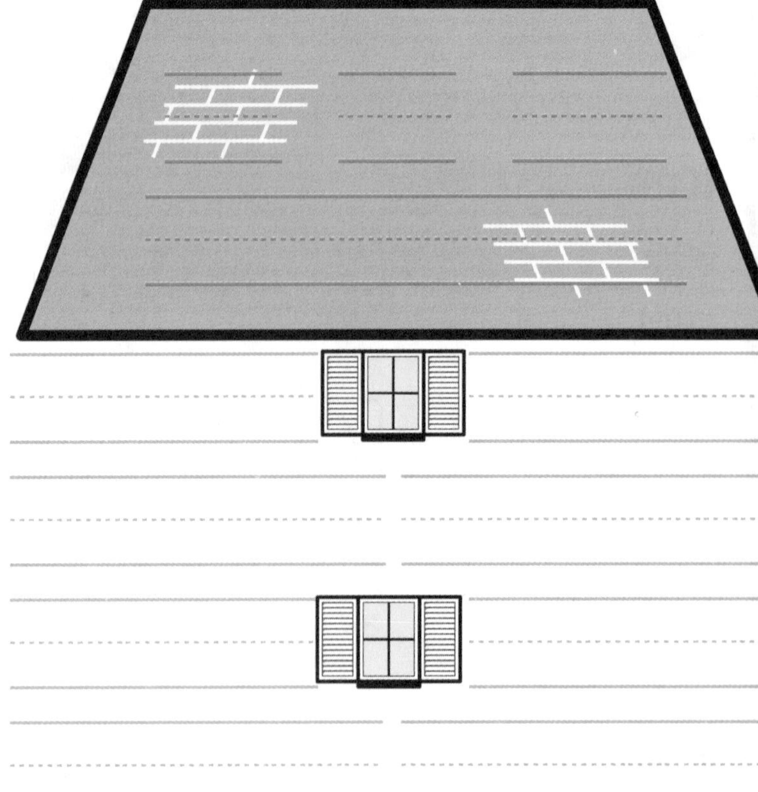

B **God's Word.** Copy this verse from Psalm 111:10a in your best handwriting. Color a pretty border around it.

"The fear of the Lord is
the beginning of wisdom."

C **Fluffy.** Ten of your words are in this story. Circle them and copy them on the lines after the story. One word is in the story twice. Copy it once.

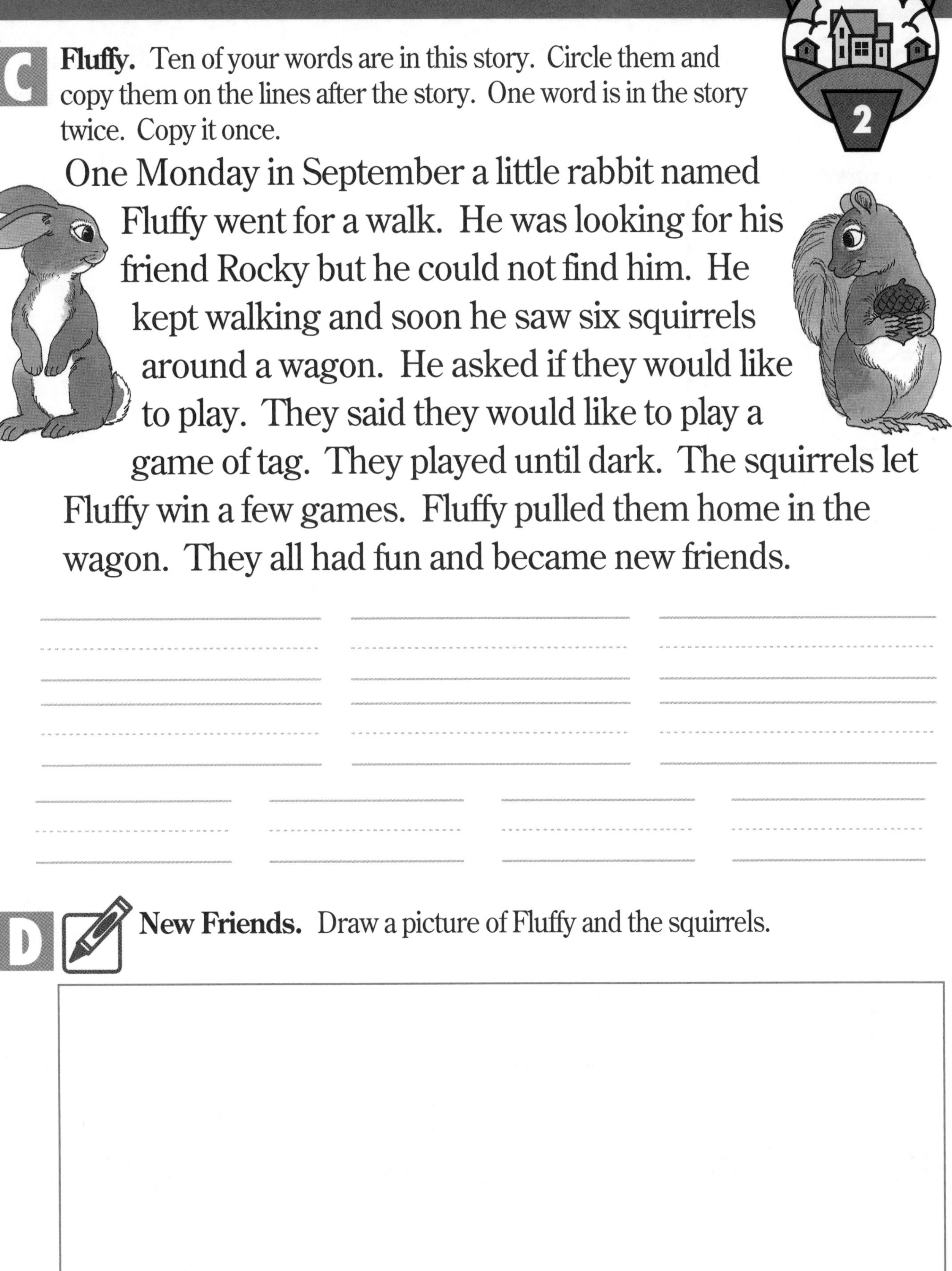

One Monday in September a little rabbit named Fluffy went for a walk. He was looking for his friend Rocky but he could not find him. He kept walking and soon he saw six squirrels around a wagon. He asked if they would like to play. They said they would like to play a game of tag. They played until dark. The squirrels let Fluffy win a few games. Fluffy pulled them home in the wagon. They all had fun and became new friends.

D **New Friends.** Draw a picture of Fluffy and the squirrels.

E **Gospel.** The word Gospel means "good news." Jesus' coming to earth is good news for everyone because He can save us. Write on the lines why Jesus is good news for you.

GOOD NEWS TIMES

F **Wisdom.** The word wisdom means "knowing what is right." The Bible says that knowing about God and Jesus makes us very wise. The way to have wisdom is to learn all you can about Jesus from the Bible, your parents, your teacher and your pastor. Write what you have learned about Jesus.

G **The Way to Go.** Write the words Gospel and wisdom two times each on the train.

☐ Have you put your Home Base Words in the Glossary? Color the box yellow if you have.

H Word Check.

Write two words that begin with capitals.

Write two words that have only two letters.

Write three words that have three letters.

Write two words that have five letters.

Write three words with six letters.

Write your Home Base Words.

of
but
if
until
rabbit
six
wagon
Monday
win
September
wisdom
gospel

I

Home Base Words. Write a sentence with each of your Home Base Words. Use your best handwriting.

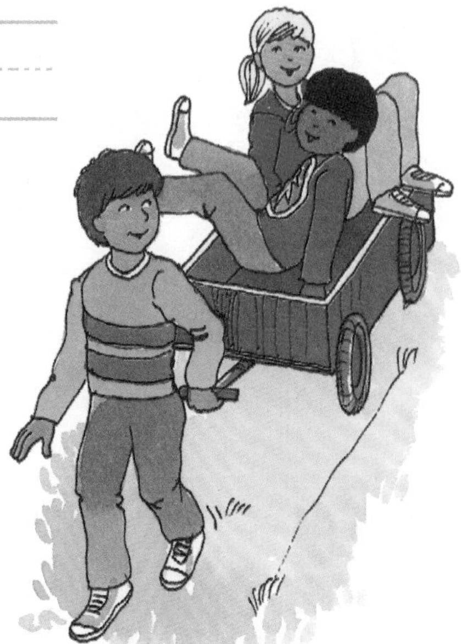

hill
full
bell
pull
baseball
shall
roll
pizza
drill
fuss
fall
mess

LESSON 3 Target: Double letters

A **Bats and Balls.** Write the list words on the bats and ball where they belong.

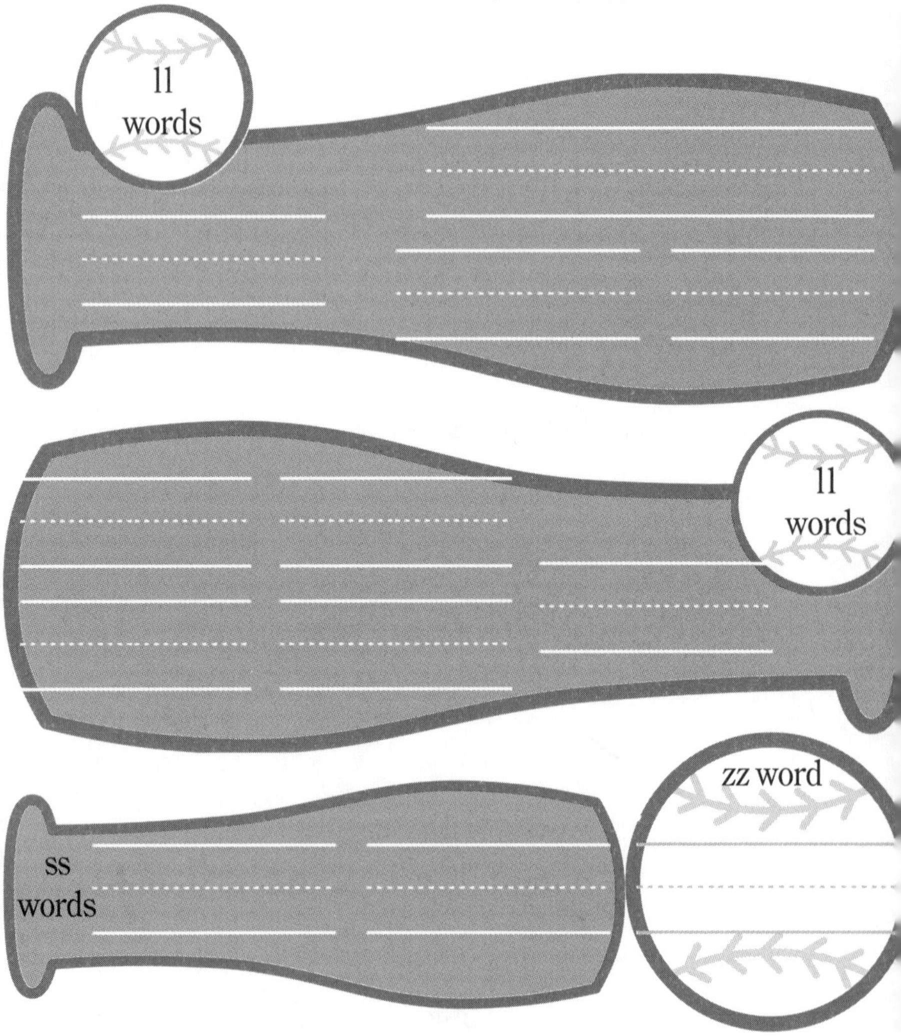

ll words

ll words

ss words

zz word

B **God's Glory.** God made a beautiful world for us to enjoy. Write Isaiah 6:3b in your best handwriting.

"The whole earth is full of His glory."

C Match It. Write the list word that goes with each picture.

D Word Drill. Write all your list words on the lines. Circle double l with red. Circle double s with green. Circle double z with blue.

☐ Have you put your Home Base Words in the Glossary? Color the box blue if you have.

E **Tony's Cat.** Use these words to finish the story.

full	mess	roll	off
fuss	shall	ball	will
fall	pull	glass	mess

Tony was in his room. He had a __________ __________ of milk on his table. His cat came into the room. He saw his cat __________ a __________ with his paw. He saw the milk start to __________ __________ the table. The milk made a big __________ on the floor. He said, "What __________ I do? Mother __________ __________ about the __________." He went to __________ out the mop to clean up the floor. His mother was proud of him for his hard work.

hill
full
bell
pull
baseball
shall
roll
pizza
drill
fuss
fall
mess

F **Art Action.** Draw a picture of Tony and his cat.

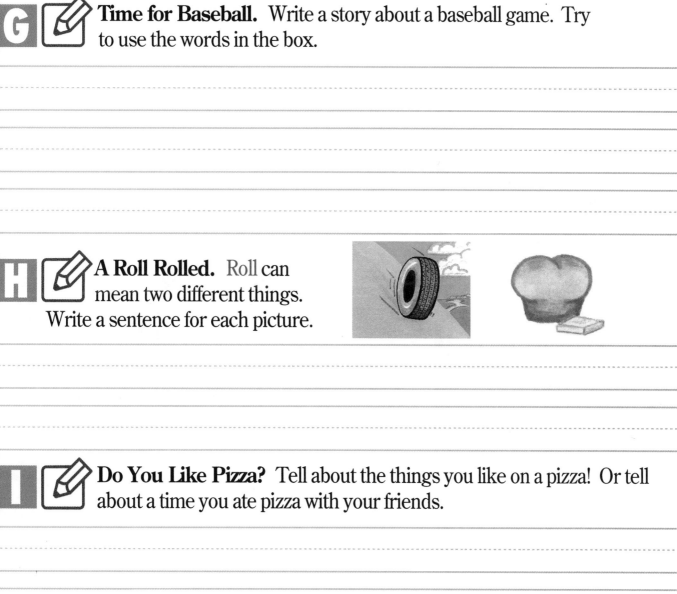

G **Time for Baseball.** Write a story about a baseball game. Try to use the words in the box.

H **A Roll Rolled.** Roll can mean two different things. Write a sentence for each picture.

I **Do You Like Pizza?** Tell about the things you like on a pizza! Or tell about a time you ate pizza with your friends.

days
have*
games
gray
safe
nose
October
pages
ropes
Tuesday
face
yoke

LESSON 4 Target: Long **a** and **o**

A **Seeing the Pattern.** The words in the list have a long or short a or a long o in them. Write them in the list where they belong. Write your Home Base Words too.

Long a

Long o

Short a

***Remember** that a final v is spelled ve.

Home Base Words

☐ Have you put your Home Base Words in the Glossary? Color the box gray if you have.

B **An Easy Yoke.** A yoke is a harness used to hook two animals together. Jesus talked about a yoke in Matthew 11:29-30. He says that we are to be a team with Him. We are to be in His yoke with Him. That makes our yoke easy. Our lives will be easier if He is helping us. Copy Matthew 11:30 in your best handwriting.

"For my yoke is easy and my burden is light."

C **Capitals.** Some special words always begin with capital letters. Tuesday is a day of the week. October is a month of the year. These always start with a capital. Write each word two times.

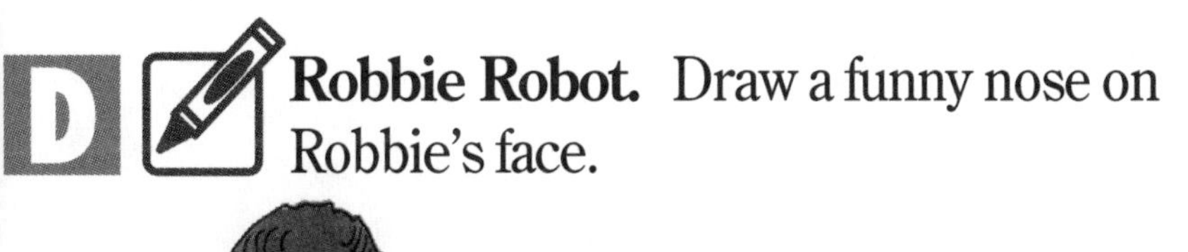

D **Robbie Robot.** Draw a funny nose on Robbie's face.

E **At the Playground.** Finish the picture and write a story about it. Try to use the words around the picture and some of your Home Base Words.

Tuesday

days

games

safe

October

have

F Crossword Puzzle.

Crossword Puzzle. Use your spelling words in the crossword puzzle.

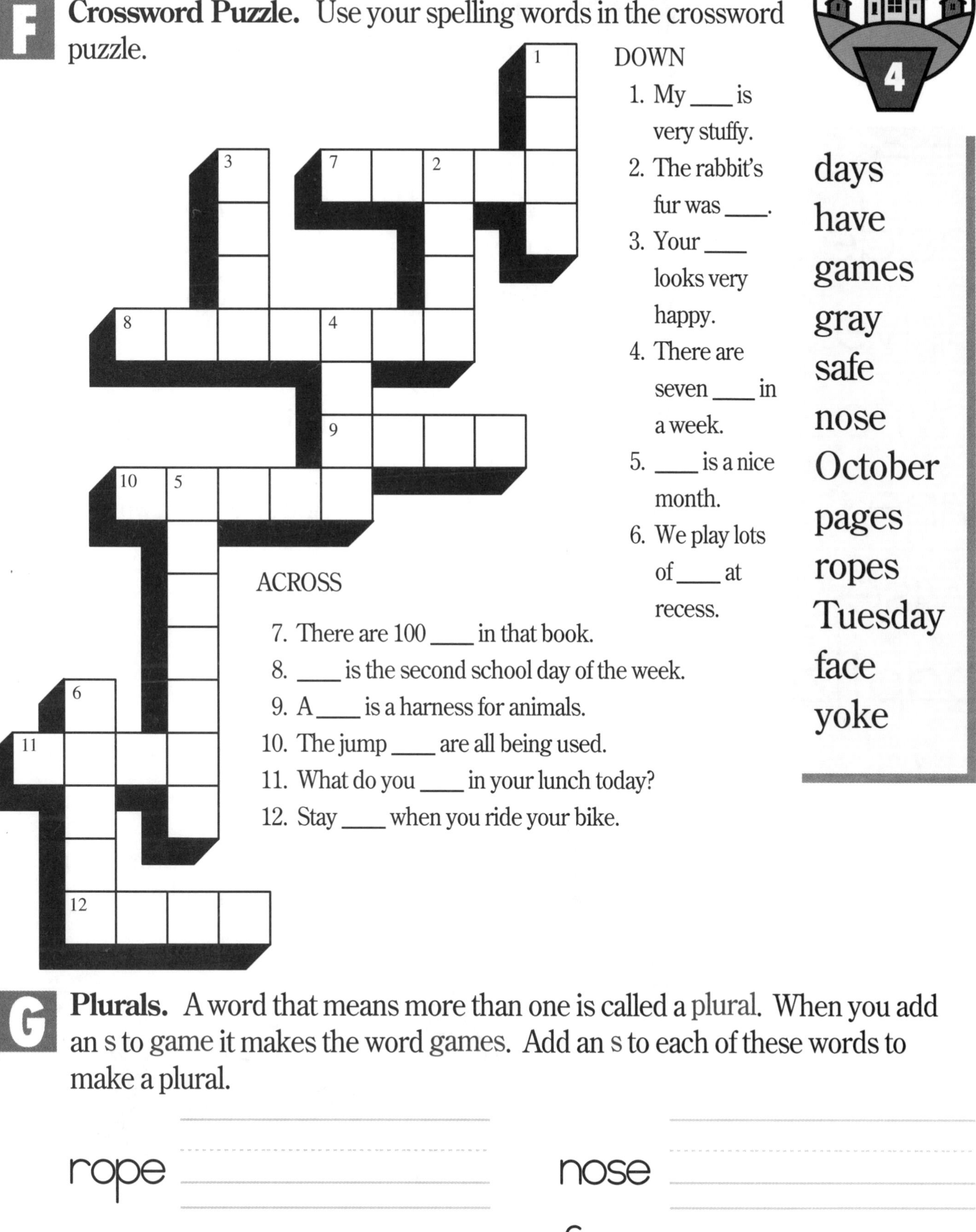

DOWN

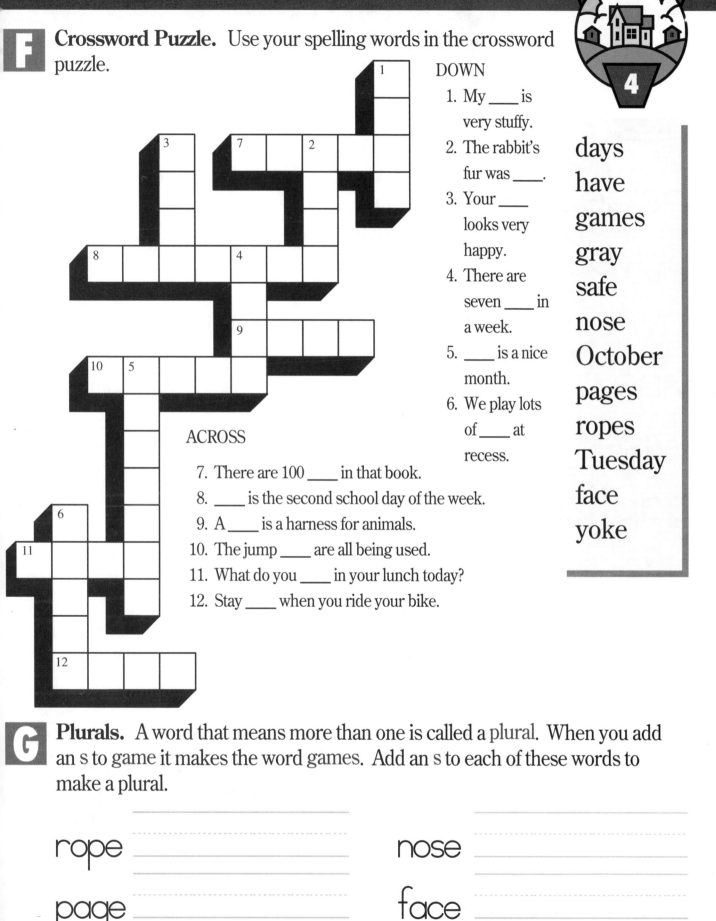

1. My ____ is very stuffy.
2. The rabbit's fur was ____.
3. Your ____ looks very happy.
4. There are seven ____ in a week.
5. ____ is a nice month.
6. We play lots of ____ at recess.

ACROSS

7. There are 100 ____ in that book.
8. ____ is the second school day of the week.
9. A ____ is a harness for animals.
10. The jump ____ are all being used.
11. What do you ____ in your lunch today?
12. Stay ____ when you ride your bike.

days
have
games
gray
safe
nose
October
pages
ropes
Tuesday
face
yoke

G Plurals.

Plurals. A word that means more than one is called a plural. When you add an s to game it makes the word games. Add an s to each of these words to make a plural.

rope ____________________ nose ____________________

page ____________________ face ____________________

Target: Long i

hides
slides
fire
inside
drive
invite
vine
wise
baptize
five
tired
surprise

A Adding E.

Write the word hid. Add an e to the word hid to make the word hide.

What happened to the i sound when you added the e?

Write the word slid. Add an e to the word slid.

What happened to the i sound when you added the e?

Write the word fir. Add an e to the word fir.

Now add an s to each word and read the new word.

B Picture Match.

Write the list words that go with the pictures. Circle the i and e in each word.

Writing. Pretend you have hidden a present for someone to find. Give two clues about how to find it.

1.

2.

Word Shapes. Write the list words that fit into the boxes.

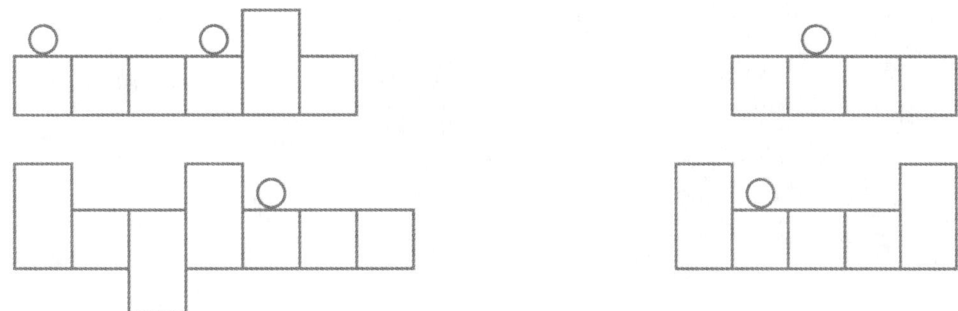

God's Word. A grape plant is a vine. In John 15, Jesus says that He is the vine and we are the branches. When we stay close to Him, we will have His help. Copy John 15:5a in your best handwriting.

"I am the vine, you are the branches."

Have you put your Home Base Words in the Glossary?
Color the leaf green if you have.

F **Lost Letters.** Fill in the missing letters to write list words.

ba___t___ze f___r___ s___rp___ ___s___

s___ ___d___s v___ ___e i___ ___it___

d___i___e wi___ ___ ___ns___d___

t___ ___ ___d ___iv___ ___id___s

G **Time for a Party.** When you invite someone to a party you send an invitation. Pretend you are having a party. Finish this invitation.

birthday party
sleep-over
surprise

Word Box

next Saturday

this Friday
at my house
at school

Who: ____________________

What: ____________________

Where: ____________________

When: ____________________

hides
slides
fire
inside
drive
invite
vine
wise
baptize
five
tired
surprise

H **Fill-Ins.** Use three of your spelling words in these sentences.

1. The ________ kept the campers warm.

2. My brother will be ________ on his birthday.

3. We were very ________ after our late night.

I **Art Action.** There is a surprise in this box. What do you think it is? Write your answer on the line and draw it inside the box.

____

J **Slide Down the Slide.** The word slides can mean two things. Copy these two sentences to find out the two meanings of slides.

The slides are fun to play on.

____

Miss Katy's car slides on the ice.

____

and
have
of
but
as
if
five
until
listen
hill
inside
pull
surprise
October
Tuesday

Target: Review Lessons 1-5

A **Word Shapes.** Write your list words in the boxes where they belong.

Short a Words

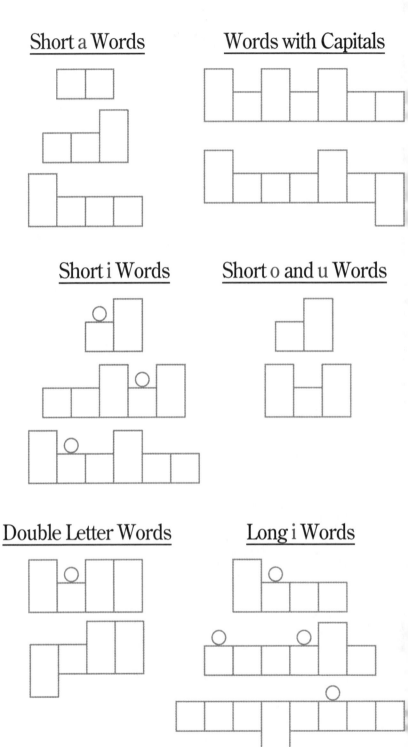

Words with Capitals

Short i Words

Short o and u Words

Double Letter Words

Long i Words

The Bible says, "You are the light of the world. A city that is set on a hill cannot be hidden." (Matthew 5:14)

B **Hide and Seek.** Circle the list word hidden in each group of letters. Write it again on the line.

qufive

lands

phavey

slisteno

rsinside

rpull

C **Sound Alikes.** Write the list word that rhymes with each of these words.

1. cut
2. has
3. hand
4. full
5. drill
6. stiff
7. drive
8. glisten

D **Capitals.** October and Tuesday both start with capital letters. Write a sentence using each word.

E **Fill-Ins.** Use list words in the sentences where they belong.

1. There is a ______________ in the box.
2. Don't come ______________ noon.
3. I want a bag ___________ chips.
4. Janie ___________ Maria are my friends.
5. Please ______________ to your teacher.
6. We like to climb the ______________.

F **ABC Order.** Put these list words in ABC order.

if pull hill but as	five of if until listen

A B C D E F G H I J K L M N O P Q R S T U V W X Y Z

G **Please Make Sense.** The underlined words in the sentences do not make sense. Write each sentence again with a list word that makes sense.

I hat two sisters.

We lick to music.

The hot was steep.

I have fire kittens.

Do you hall a penny?

Wait under noon to eat.

The game is into the box.

and
have
of
but
as
if
five
until
listen
hill
inside
pull
surprise
October
Tuesday

LESSON 7 Target: Final **k** and **ck**

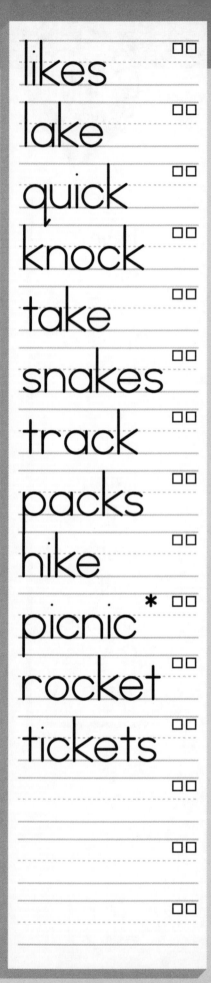

likes
lake
quick
knock
take
snakes
track
packs
hike
picnic *
rocket
tickets

A **Pick a C or K.** Write the words in the right list. Circle the letter or letters that make the k sound.

c Word	ck Words	k Words

Home Base Words

B **Time for a Picnic.** If you were going on a picnic, what would you pack in the basket? Write four things and draw one in the basket.

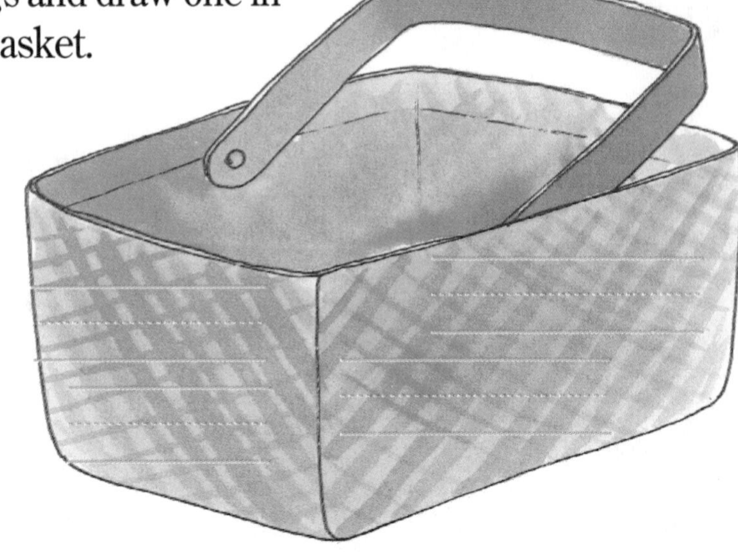

likes take
lake snakes
picnic hike
packs

C **Maria's Hike.** Use the words from the box in the story.

Maria __________ to go on walks with her family.

They often __________ to a __________ in the

woods. They carry a __________ lunch. Maria

__________ the picnic with her mother. They

__________ lots of food! Sometimes they see

__________. They always have fun.

D **Your Hike.** Have you ever been on a hike?

____

Write hike two times.

____

____

Draw a picture of a hike.

E **God's Word.** Jesus says that He stands at the door of our hearts and knocks. We must decide if we will let Him come into our lives. He will not come in unless He has been invited. Have you invited Him in? Write in a list word to complete Revelation 3:20a.

"Behold, I stand at the door and ________."

F **A Rocket Ride.** Here is a ticket for a rocket ride.

ADMIT
ROCKET RIDE
EARTH TO
PLANET MARS
TUESDAY
JULY 10, 2175
7:30 AM
ONE

Where is the rocket going? ________

What day of the week is it going? ________

What is the date of the ride? ________

What time does it take off? ________

What year does it go? ________

Write rocket and ticket. ________ ________

G **Write About It.** Would you like to go on a rocket ride some day? Write a sentence about it.

USA

☐ Have you put your Home Base Words in the Glossary? Color the box red if you have.

H Meanings Match.

Meanings Match. Write the list words that match these meanings.

1. fast
2. what a train runs on
3. a packed lunch
4. reptiles that hiss
5. a large pool of water
6. to rap on a door

likes
lake
quick
knock
take
snakes
track
packs
hike
picnic
rocket
tickets

I Quick Work.

Quick Work. Write about some quick work you can do, like getting your backpacks ready to go home.

J Art Action.

Art Action. Draw a picture of you doing the quick work.

K Home Base Words.

Home Base Words. Write your Home Base Words on the lines two times each.

doing

two

too

could

would

into

soon

move

November*

poor

bedroom

good-bye

LESSON 8 Target: Short and long oo

A **One or Two.** Write the list words where they belong.

One o	**Two o's**

The letter o is a funny letter! Say the list words and listen to the sounds o makes. If the word has a short oo like wood put a red box around it. If it has a long oo like food put a blue circle around it. November has a long o sound. Do not mark it.

B **Word Find.** Circle your list words in the Word Find.

a i b N o v e m b e r d e j g b
l t o o c g a m c w o u l d o o
o n h s j p c j n d e m f p o m
p d b o l d o i n g s o l o d h
n i f o h i u e g a h v t o b r
f m e n a o l f b i k e p r y j
k i n t o r d d m t w o c h e s
c o e m b e d r o o m l n e g i
r k b s n t i k r u g v d s t o

LESSON 8

C Word Check.

1. Two words rhyme with should. When you learn the spelling of one, you will know the spelling of all three words. Write the three rhyming words.

_______________ _______________ _______________

2. The words two, too, and to sound alike but they have different meanings and spellings. They are called homophones. Write them correctly in the sentences.

Billy went _____ the store. He said, "I would like _____ cookies. I want some ice cream, _____ .

3. Three words are compounds. They are made from two smaller words. Put your compound words by their meanings.

what to say when you are ready to go _______________

a place where you sleep _______________

entering = going _______________ a room

4. One word has the suffix ing. Write do, doing, or did in these sentences.

I will _________ all my work before lunch.

Mark is _________ his work now.

Karen _________ her work yesterday.

D Home Base Words. Write your Home Base Words in sentences.

E **Which Month?** November is the name of a month. It always starts with a capital letter. Write November two times.

You have spelled the names of three months. Read the clue and write the name of the month.

This month begins with a capital S.

This month begins with a capital O.

This month begins with a capital N.

F **Number Words.** You have spelled five number words. Write the word that goes with the number.

7

10 5

6 2

G **Glossary Check.** Look up doing and poor in the Glossary. Copy the sentence for each word in your best handwriting.

☐ Have you put your Home Base Words in the Glossary? Color the box purple if you have

H **Story Writing.** Use these words in the story.

would could
good-bye into
poor two
move soon
bedroom

________ Greg! He felt sad because he had to ________ .

He ________ have to say ________ to his ________

best friends. He went ________ his ________ and sat on his

bed. ________ the moving van would come. What

________ Greg do to feel better? Write your answer.

doing
two
too
could
would
into
soon
move
November
poor
bedroom
good-bye

I **God's Help.** Jesus helps us when we are sad. The Bible says, "Be anxious for nothing, but in everything by prayer and supplication, with thanksgiving, let your requests be made known to God." (Philippians 4:6)

What are you sometimes sad about? Ask Jesus in prayer to help you. Draw a picture of yourself praying.

with
that
three
this
then
should
both
thick
shoes
Thursday
wishes
washes

A **Sound and Form Check.** When h is added to s or t it makes a new sound. Write your list words in their shapes.

B **Home Base Words.** Draw shape boxes for your Home Base Words. Trace all the shape boxes with a blue crayon. Do it again with a red crayon.

C **Meanings Match.** Fill in your list words that match these meanings.

a number

not thin

not this

not that

your wants

a day of the week

boots and sandals

D **Fill Ins.** Use a list word to finish each sentence.

1. Lee ______________ sit still.
2. Mother ______________ my clothes.
3. I played, ______________ I ate my dinner.
4. Marie went ______________ her sister.
5. ______________ Mike and Todd can go.

E **ABC Order.** Put these th words in ABC order. Look at the third letter for your clue.

then this three that

A B C D E F G H I J K L M N O P Q R S T U V W X Y Z

F **Lost Letters.** Fill in the missing letters for these words. Trace all the letters. Say the words to yourself after you write them.

___ ___ree	___ ___is	___ ___ick
bo___ ___	___ ___at	___ ___en
wa___ ___es	wi___ ___es	___ ___ursday
___ ___oes	___ ___ould	wi___ ___

G **God's Promise.** Jesus promises to always be with us. He will never leave us. In Matthew 28:20 He says,

"Lo, I am with you always, even to the end of the age."

Write some sentences thanking Jesus for always being with you.

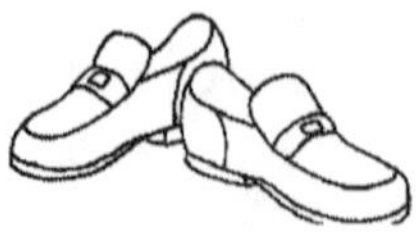

Have you put your Home Base Words in the Glossary?
Color the shoes orange if you have.

LESSON 9

H **Story Time.** Write a story about something that happened to Mike on a Thursday. Use as many of the list words and Home Base Words as you can.

with
that
three
this
then
should
both
thick
shoes
Thursday
wishes
washes

I **Word Check.** Color one box for every list word and Home Base Word you used in the story.

J **Life Check.** The Bible says, "This is the day which the Lord has made. We will rejoice and be glad in it." (Psalm 118:24)

What has happened to you today that is good?

Draw a picture for your sentence.

what
when
white
while
which
why
such
chocolate
benches
chosen
lunchroom
church

LESSON 10 Target: Words with **wh** and **ch**

A **Sorting Sounds.** Write the list words on the cake. Write the words with ch on the bottom. Write the words with wh in the middle and write the Home Base Words on the top.

Home Base Words

wh

ch

B **Snowball.** You have a color word in the list this week. Write the word two times by the picture that gives you a clue.

LESSON 10

C **Sentences.** Look up lunchroom and benches in the Glossary. Read the sentence for each one. Write a new sentence for lunchroom and benches.

D **Questions.** Who, whom, what, when, why and which are question words. Answer these questions.

Who loves you? ____

Whom do you love? ____

What do you want to be when you grow up? ____

When is your birthday? ____

Why do you like school? ____

Which school do you go to? ____

what
when
white
while
which
why
such
chocolate
benches
chosen
lunchroom
church

E **A Place to Worship.** Write the word three times that means a place to worship God and be together with other Christians.

What is the name of your church?

F **The Chocolate Planet.** Most people like chocolate. Write a story about a planet made of chocolate. Use as many list words as you can. Draw a picture of the chocolate planet.

LESSON 10

G **The Bible Says:**

"The God of our fathers has chosen you that you should know His will." (Acts 22:14a)

Write a thank-you note to God for letting you be His special child.

H **Fill–Ins.** Use the correct words in the sentences.

such chosen while white

The brown puppy was ____________ first. The other puppies made ____________ a fuss when he left. They were barking ____________ they waited to be chosen. The ____________ puppy was the last one to go to a new home.

PETS

I **Home Base Words.** Write a sentence for each of your Home Base Words.

Color the church white if you put your Home Base Words in the Glossary.

there*
been*
where*
here
seen
teeth
these
Wednesday*
cheese
weekend
need
eve

LESSON 11 Target: Long **e**

ee ere

A Working with Words.

1. You have learned that an e added to a word can make a vowel long.
   tap — tape   hop — hope
   Try this one: her — ________
2. Another word with the silent e means short time before something happens.
   ____
3. Sometimes you will see the long e spelled ee as in see or feet. Spell the e words from your list.
   a. I saw it. Have you ________ it
   b. I ________ another pencil.
   c. Brush your ________ after dinner.
   d. Those books are Liz's. ________ books are mine.

LESSON 11

4. Write another word for Saturday and Sunday.

   We will play this ____________________.

   Did you notice this compound word meaning the end of the week?

5. One word spelled ee but spoken with a short e means past time for be.

   We have ____________ working hard.

6. Two words are related to here.

   One asks. ________________

   One tells. ________________

7. One word is the middle day of the week. ________________

8. Now you have spelled all the list words. Write your Home Base Words on these lines.

   ________________ ________________ ________________

B **Days of the Week.** You have spelled four days of the week. Write each day two times.

M ________________ ________________

T ________________ ________________

W ________________ ________________

Th ________________ ________________

Robbie Robot. Draw some funny teeth for Robbie.

C **The Night Before.** The word eve means the time just before something happens. We use Eve most often as a woman's name or a part of a special name. It usually has a capital. Remember Eve in the Bible? See Eve in Christmas Eve and New Year's Eve. Use eve in a sentence. Use a capital if you use it as a name.

D **Um! Um! Good!** Cheese is a great food! Draw three pictures of things made with cheese. Label the pictures. Write a sentence about your favorite picture.

E **Here, There, Where.** These words tell places where things are. Use them in the sentences where they belong.

W________ is your coat?

H________ is a prize for you.

T________ were four puppies in the box.

Remember: Here is in there and where!

F **The First Woman.** God created Adam and Eve and made a beautiful garden for them to live in. He wanted them to be happy there forever. But because they sinned they had to leave the garden. Write this Bible verse from Genesis 3:20 in your best handwriting and draw a picture of Adam and Eve in their garden home.

"Adam named his wife Eve, because she would become the mother of all the living."

there
been
where
here
seen
teeth
these
Wednesday
cheese
weekend
need
eve

Color the cheese yellow if you put your Home Base Words in the Glossary this week.

likes ☐☐
there ☐☐
doing ☐☐
with ☐☐
what ☐☐
when ☐☐
two ☐☐
too ☐☐
then ☐☐
been ☐☐
could ☐☐
would ☐☐
should ☐☐
where ☐☐
white ☐☐

LESSON 12 Target: Review Lessons 7-11

A

Mix–Ups. These words are all mixed up! Fix them so that they spell list words.

kelis	idong	oto
________	________	________
ldouc	wot	wolud
________	________	________
hiwt	neht	loshdu
________	________	________
reteh	ietwh	nehw
________	________	________
twah	nebe	herew
________	________	________

B

Replacements. Write the list word that means the same as the underlined part of the sentence.

1. Mark <u>enjoys</u> ice cream. ________
2. We are <u>working</u> puzzles. ________
3. My dog has <u>2</u> puppies. ________
4. The bunnies are <u>not black</u>. ________

C **Missing Words.** Write the list word that is missing from the sentence.

1. Can you go to the store __________ me?
2. We went to school and __________ we went home.
3. My brother __________candy.
4. I like candy,__________ .
5. Janice has __________ to the beach before.
6. There are __________ brown puppies in the box.
7. __________ the mail comes, I will get it.
8. You are __________ a good job.
9. __________is my baseball mitt?
10. The new snow was very__________ .
11. __________ is your favorite food?
12. __________are ten girls in our class.

D **Could, Would, and Should.** Remember the special spelling of these words. Write a sentence for each one. Underline the list word in each sentence.

1.

2.

3.

E **God's Word.** The Bible says, "For where two or three are gathered together in My name, I am there in the midst of them." (Matthew 18:20)

This means that Jesus is with us when we meet together to worship Him. Draw a picture of where you like to be with other people who love Jesus.

Questions. Some of the words in your list are usually question words. Use these words to write three questions.

what where when

likes
there
doing
with
what
when
two
too
then
been
could
would
should
where
white

Now, trade books with a friend. Write the answers to your friend's questions.

leave
please
believe
piece
meat
December
peace
team
really
creation
eats
each

LESSON 13 Target: More long e

A **Spellings of Long E.** Long e can be spelled different ways. In Lesson 11, you studied ee and e consonant e. Put in the missing letters that make the long e sound in these list words.

l____ve	p____ce	pl____se
t____m	p____ce	r____lly
bel____ve	cr____ation	m____t
____ts	D____cember	____ch

Long e is spelled three ways in the list words. What are they?

________ ________ ________

B **Sound Alikes.** Homophones are words that sound alike but have different spellings and meanings. Write the list word that goes with these meanings.

1. A small part of a pie is called a ________.
2. To be friendly and happy with another person is to be at ________.
3. Hamburgers and chicken are kinds of ________.
4. Do you know the homophone for meat? It means to be introduced to someone. ________

Color the gift green if you put your Home Base Words in the Glossary.

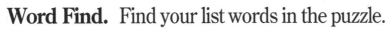

C Word Find. Find your list words in the puzzle.

```
n i e c e e l e a p e a m e a n
e D e b e v e n a p p l e a s e
a c r e a t i o n e i e a e e a
r e a l l y l e a n e a t s e c
c e a i f e e l m e c v D e n h
l b D e c e m b e r e e t r e e
e e e v e a s t l r e c e i v e
a e p e a c e i s l e e p y b e
h s f l e a t e a m c r e a m e
```

There are many more long e words in your puzzle. See how many you can find.

D Months of the Year. You have spelled the names of four months. Write the name of the month beside the clue.

School usually starts in ______________________.

Columbus Day is in ______________________.

Thanksgiving is in ______________________.

Christmas is in ______________________.

Did you start each month with a capital? ____________

E ABC Order. Put these list words in ABC order.

eats really each meat leave team believe please

1. ______________ 4. ______________ 7. ______________

2. ______________ 5. ______________ 8. ______________

3. ______________ 6. ______________

F **December Days.** Draw a picture about December in the box. Write a story about your picture on the lines.

LESSON 13

SCHOOL

G **God's Gift.** John 3:16 says, "For God so loved the world that He gave His only begotten Son, that whoever believes in Him should not perish but have everlasting life." Write a note to Jesus thanking Him for coming to earth to save you.

Dear Jesus,

Love,

- leave
- please
- believe
- piece
- meat
- December
- peace
- team
- really
- creation
- eats
- each

H **Word Exchange.** Replace each lightly printed word with a list word that has the same meaning.

1. My brother is ___very___ nice to me.
2. I ___trust___ in Jesus.
3. Miss Haas gave ___every___ child a gift.
4. ___Kindly___ place your books inside your desks.
5. We will ___go from___ school at 3 o'clock.
6. My basketball ___group___ will practice today.
7. We enjoy looking at God's ___handiwork___.

I **Write About It.** Write one of your Home Base Words in a sentence.

they
said*
gave
today
eight
paid
grade
played
praise
behave
faith
Savior

LESSON 14 Target: Long a

A **Spellings for Long A.** There are many ways to spell the long a sound. Write the list words in the boxes and color over the letters that make the long a sound with a yellow crayon or marker. Sometimes there is a consonant between the a and e that make the long a sound. One word does not have a long a sound.

Write the remaining word. This word comes from say. It does not have a long a.

B **Knowing God.** Put these list words in the sentences where they belong.

faith praise paid Savior

Jesus ____________ the price for our sins

____________ means trusting in Jesus

Jesus is our ____________.

We are to ____________ Him every da

C Working with Words.

1. The word behave has the little word have in it. Say the word behave and say the word have. Do they sound alike? ________
   Fill in the right words.

   a. Mother said, "Please ______________ yourself."

   b. "May I ___________ some milk, please?"

2. The name of the month of May has a long a sound in it spelled ay. Two more list words have ay in them. Write all three ay words. Circle the ay.

   ______________ ______________ ______________

3. Said means past time for say. Fill in both words.

   a. Mother __________ to tell you, "Hello."

   b. I can __________ the alphabet.

4. Three list words use ai to spell the long a. Write the ai words. Circle the ai.

   ______________ ______________ ______________

5. Three list words have a consonant between the a and e to make the long a sound. Write them. Circle the a and e.

   ______________ ______________ ______________

6. Four words show past time. Write your related list word.

   play ______________ pay ______________

   give ______________ say ______________

D **Match Ups.** Write the list word that matches each picture.

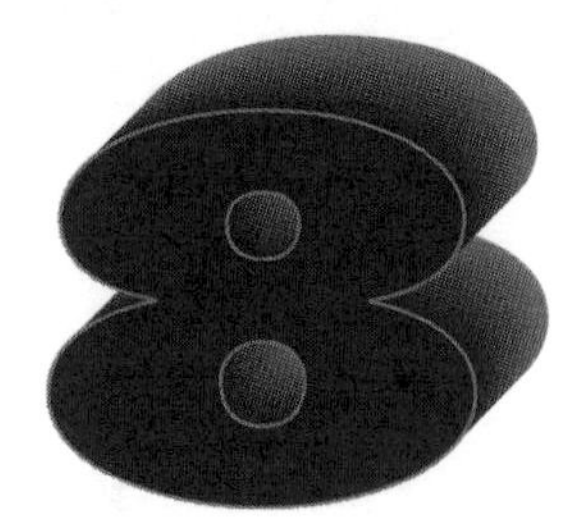

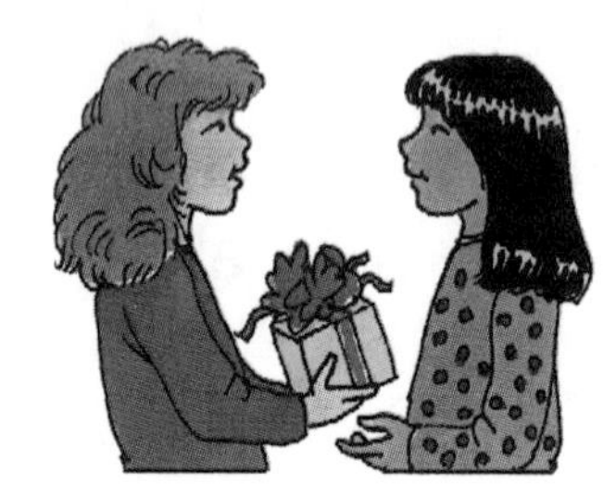

E **Glossary Check.** Look up today and they in the Glossary. Write a new sentence for each word.

F **Number Names.** Write the name of each of these numerals.

8 ______ 6 ______

2 ______ 3 ______

5 ______ 7 ______

10 ______

G **School Work.** Write a story about the picture at the bottom of the page. Try to use some of the words that are in the box beside the picture.

they
said
gave
today
eight
paid
grade
played
praise
behave
faith
Savior

they
behave
gave
said
today
played
grade
eight

LESSON 15 Target: Long o

one*
some*
know
open
above*
yellow
those
grow
goes
roses
coat
roadway

A **In Its Place.** Write the list words on the roses. See how many ways the long o sound is spelled.

Home Base Words. Use each of your Home Base Words in a sentence.

B **Sound Alikes.** Homophones are words that sound alike but have different meanings and different spellings. Write a homophone in the second sentence for the red word.

There is no person here.

I ________________ the Lord is with me.

The sum of one plus one is two.

Here is ________________ cake for you.

Our team won the game.

My cousin is ________________ year old.

C **Meanings.** One of your list words means to be <u>over</u> something. Write it on the line.

____

Draw a picture of birds above a lake.

One of your list words means that something is <u>not closed</u>. Write it on the line.

____

Draw a picture of an open book.

One of your list words is <u>something for cars to drive on</u>. Write it on the line.

____

Draw a picture of a car on a roadway.

D **Gifts from the Heart.** Sometimes it is nice to give people something just because you love them. Write a list of people to whom you would like to give a gift. After their names write the thing you would like to give. Maybe it would be helping your mother with grocery shopping or your brother with his homework.

Name	Gift

Every good gift and every perfect gift is from above.
—James 1:17a

E **Rhymes.** What list words rhyme with these pictures? Write them below the pictures.

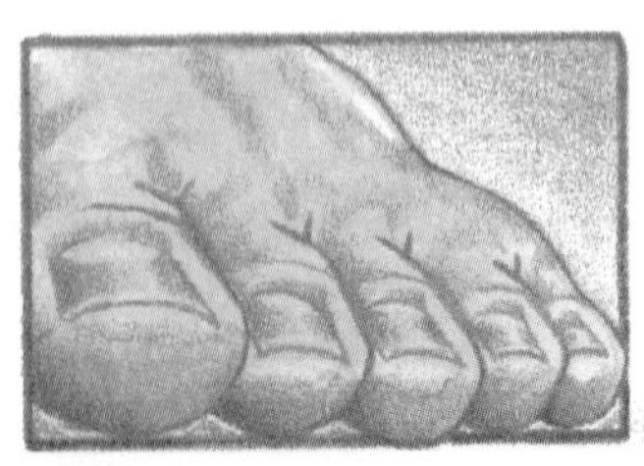

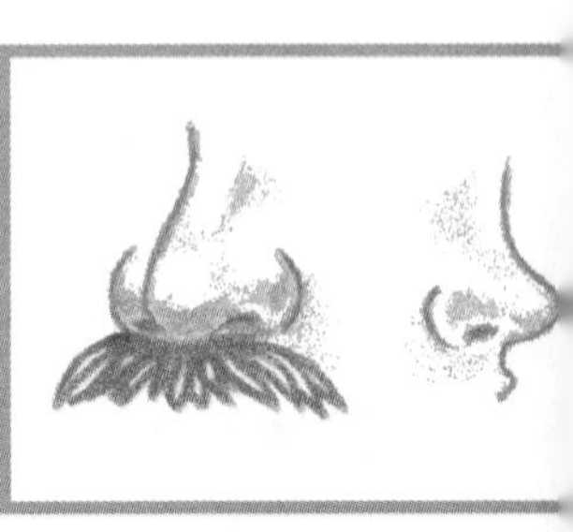

Coded Message. Use this code to write some of your list words.

a = 1	f = 6	k = 11	p = 16	u = 21
b = 2	g = 7	l = 12	q = 17	v = 22
c = 3	h = 8	m = 13	r = 18	w = 23
d = 4	i = 9	n = 14	s = 19	x = 24
e = 5	j = 10	o = 15	t = 20	y = 25
				z = 26

11–14–15–23	3–15–1–20	19–15–13–5
25–5–12–12–15–23	15–16–5–14	7–15–5–19
18–15–19–5–19	7–18–15–23	1–2–15–22–5
20–8–15–19–5	15–14–5	18–15–1–4–23–1–25

one
some
know
open
above
yellow
those
grow
goes
roses
coat
roadway

Turn About. Now it is your turn. Choose three words and write them in the code. Ask a friend to write the words.

Your Friend's Name:

More Coded Messages. Write a coded message to a friend on a piece of paper. Give it to your friend to figure out.

Color the flowers yellow if you put the Home Base Words in the Glossary this week.

right
high
try
life
buy
might
Friday
Christmas*
pie
nineteen
science
Christ

LESSON 16 Target: Long i

A **Pies for Sale.** Write your long i list words on the Christmas pies where they belong. Write one list word that has a short i on the sign.

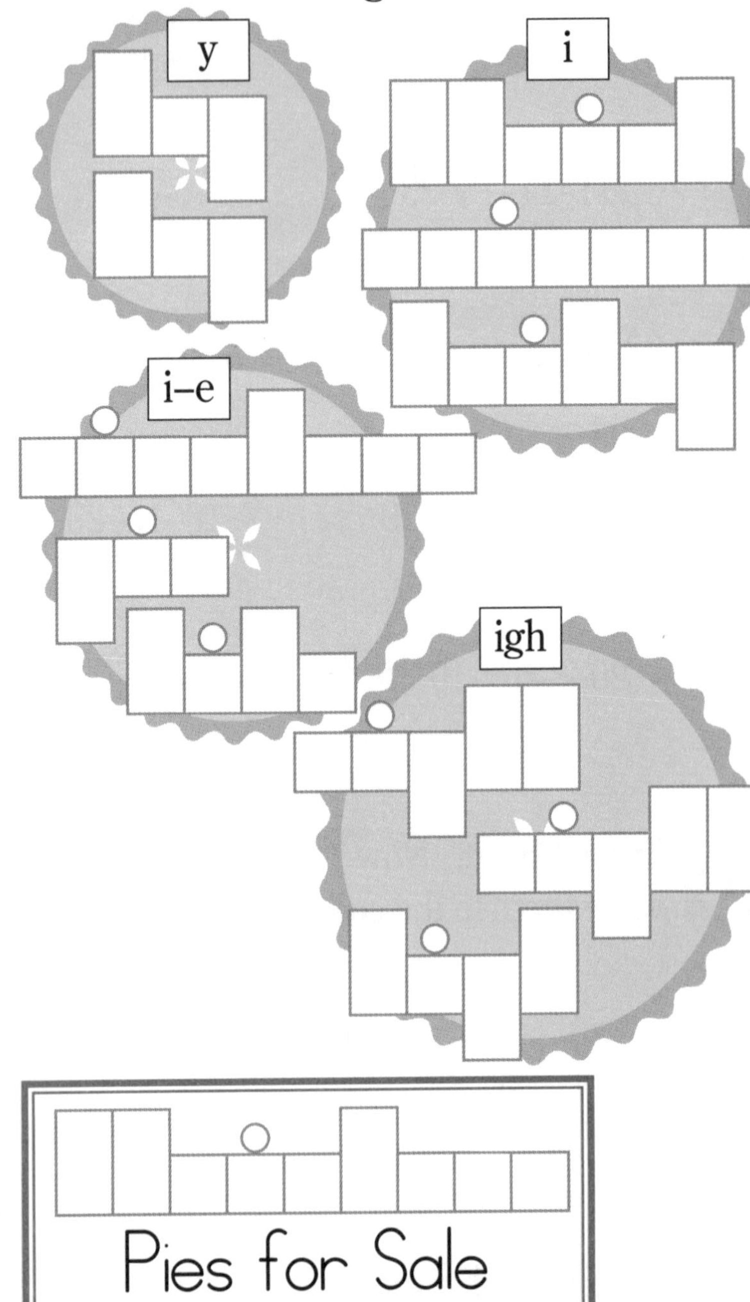

B **Color Check.** Go back and color with yellow the letters that make the long i sound.

Color the pie light brown if you put your Home Base Words in the Glossary.

C **Christ in Christmas.** If you look at the word Christmas you will see the smaller word Christ. Christ is one of Jesus' names. Christmas is Jesus' birthday. When you celebrate Christmas, be sure Jesus is the center of your celebration. Copy this Christmas verse from Luke 2:11 in your best handwriting.

"For there is born to you this day in the city of David a Savior, who is Christ the Lord."

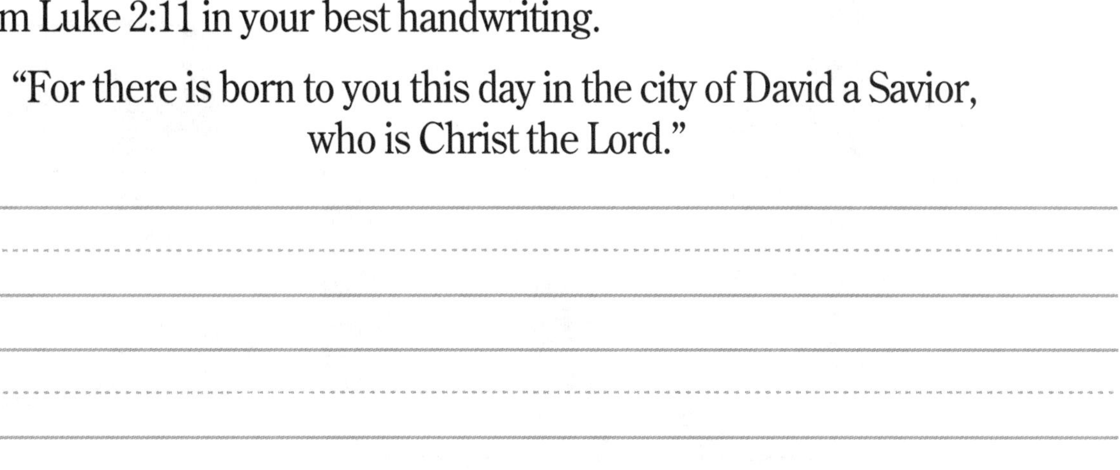

D **Cartoon Story.** Try to use the words right, high, try, might, and buy as you complete the cartoons.

E Crossword Puzzle. Use your list words in the crossword puzzle.

ACROSS

1. The last day of the school week
2. Way up in the air
3. To work hard on something
4. A special holiday in December
5. A dessert with a crust
6. To be alive is to have this
7. A subject in school

DOWN

1. The opposite of left
2. To get something with money
3. One of Jesus' names
4. My grandma ______ come today if it's sunny.
5. The number before twenty

LESSON 16

F **Root Words.** Root words are the small words that form the base of longer words.

1. Christ is the root word of Christmas. Write Christ and Christmas. Circle the root word in Christmas.

_______________ _______________

2. Write nineteen twice. Circle the long i root word in nineteen.

_______________ _______________

right
high
try
life
buy
might
Friday
Christmas
pie
nineteen
science
Christ

G **Fill–Ins.** Write in the list word which fits each sentence.

a. We went to the store to __________ a gift.

b. We always have __________ right after lunch.

c. Dad said we __________ go to the game tonight.

d. Mrs. Donaldson said for us to __________ harder.

e. I want to live my __________ for the Lord.

f. Don't throw the ball so __________.

H **Days of the Week.** You have written the names of all five weekdays. Write them below in the shape boxes. Look in the Glossary if you need help.

I **Home Base Words.** Use two of your Home Base Words in a sentence.

blue
flew
truth
January
music
rules
June
used
true
cute
yours*
drew

Target: Words with **u**, **ue**, and **ew**

A

Work with Words. The long u and long oo sounds are spelled several different ways in your list words.

1. Two words have ue. Write the words and circle the ue.

2. Four words have u consonant e. Write the words and circle the u and e.

3. Two words have ew. Write the words and circle the ew.

4. Three words have just u. Write these words and circle the u.

B

Unique U. One word has an oor sound. Think about the root word of yours. It is you. You has a long u sound. Write you, your and yours in the sentences.

I like ________. I want to be ________ friend. I think this record is ________.

C **Months of the Year.** January and June are months of the year. Write a sentence about each month. Draw a picture to go with each sentence.

D **How to Say It.** In the Glossary there are markings to show how to say your list words. They look like this: January (jan′ ū wer′ ē). Write your list words next to their pronunciations.

________	(mū′ zik)	________	(ūzd)
________	(tro͞o)	________	(dro͞o)
________	(kūt)	________	(flo͞o)

What is the marking for the long oo sound? ________

What is the marking for the long u sound? ________

Color the musical notes blue if you put your Home Base Words in the Glossary this week.

E **Relatives.** True is the root word of truth. Put these two words in the sentences where they belong.

Always tell your parents the ____________________ .

The answer to that question is ____________________ .

F **Songs of Praise.** Music is very important in the Bible. The verses in Psalms were probably songs that people sang and played. Write the words to a song that could go with this verse in Psalm 98:1a. Tell the Lord what you praise Him for.

"Oh, sing to the Lord a new song!
For He has done marvelous things."

blue
flew
truth
January
music
rules
June
used
true
cute
yours
drew

G Completing the Story. Use these words in this story.

blue flew truth rules used true drew

The ________ in the forest said that only ________ birds could fly to the tallest trees to look for crows. The red birds didn't think this was fair. They said, "We can fly fast and high. We should be ________ to help, too."

The wise owl said, "What the red birds say is ________. We will draw straws each day to see which color will be our lookouts."

From that day on they ________ straws each morning and the birds who won ________ to the tallest tree to watch.

This story tells the ________. Who you are inside is important—not what color or size you are on the outside.

H Colorful Words. You have learned four color words so far this year. Write the name of each color you see. Look in the Glossary if you need help.

one
they
some
right
blue
said
high
know
please
believe
today
Savior
Friday
January
June

LESSON 18 Target: Review Lessons 13-17

A **Sky Watch.** Look at the clouds high in this blue June sky. Put the list words in the clouds where they belong. Outline the 12 words that have long vowel sounds in pink.

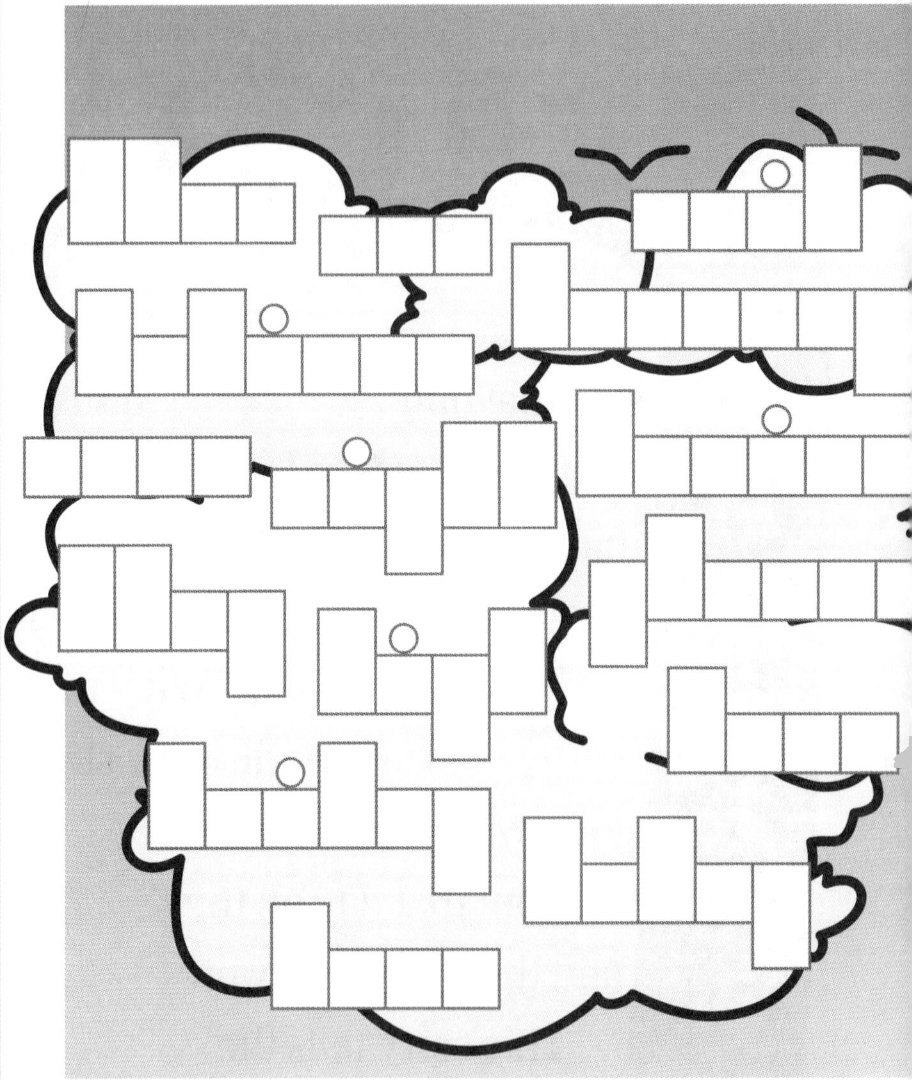

B **Capitals.** Four of the list words begin with capital letters. Write the list word that fits the meaning.

1. The sixth month: ____________
2. The One who saves us: ____________
3. The first month: ____________
4. The sixth day: ____________

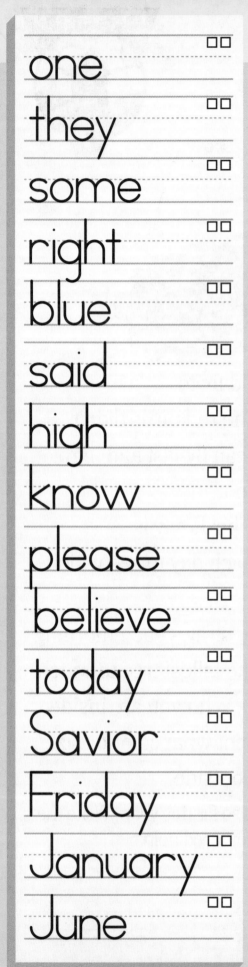

C **Making Sense.** The underlined words do not make sense in the sentence. Write the spelling word that makes sense on the numbered line.

1. I use my <u>red</u> hand to write with.
2. Mary and Martha said <u>them</u> loved Jesus.
3. There are <u>sorry</u> plates on the shelf.
4. <u>Toes</u> is my birthday.
5. I <u>knot</u> how to spell.
6. The hat is <u>hot</u> on the shelf.
7. The sky is <u>blind</u> today.
8. Here is <u>only</u> pizza.

1. ____________________

2. ____________________

3. ____________________

4. ____________________

5. ____________________

6. ____________________

7. ____________________

8. ____________________

D **Words for Life.** Write this sentence in your best handwriting. Decorate around the sentence.

If I believe in the Savior, I will have everlasting life.

E

Riddles. Write the list word that goes with each riddle.

1. I am more than zero but less than two. What am I?

   ____

2. I am never wrong. I am the opposite of left. What am I?

   ____

3. I am never nothing but always something. What am I?

   ____

4. I am after yesterday and before tomorrow. What am I?

   ____

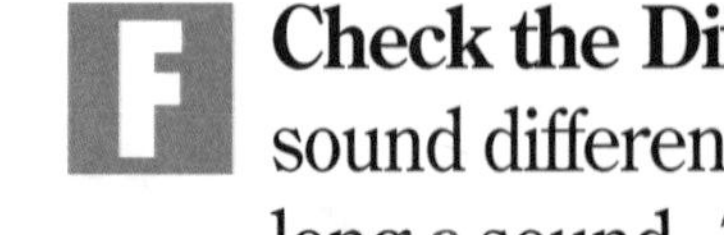

F

Check the Difference. Sometimes words are spelled almost alike but they sound differently. Look at said and paid. Said has a short e sound. Paid has a long a sound. They use the same letters but they do not sound alike. Add letters to these words to make new words. Listen to the new sound in each word.

be + have = ______________

st + one = ______________

Take letters away from these words and listen to the new sound.

they – y = ______________

know – k = ______________

cute – e = ______________

Now look for the ten differences in the two pictures.

LESSON 18

G

Something Blue. Write a story about **blue** things. Draw the **blue** things in the box after you write your story.

one
they
some
right
blue
said
high
know
please
believe
today
Savior
Friday
January
June

H

Homophones. Write the list words that sound just like these words but are spelled differently.

sum	____	Hi!	____
won	____	no	____
write	____	blew	____

Target: Putting It All Together

it's
began
myself
sometimes
I'll
Sunday
lion
hello
zero
haven't
she's
telephone
shoelace
sailboat
eyelids

A Compounds. Compound words are made from two small words put together. Write your six compound words.

B Contractions. Contractions are two words put together with some letters left out. An apostrophe takes the place of the missing letters. Write your four contractions in the shape boxes.

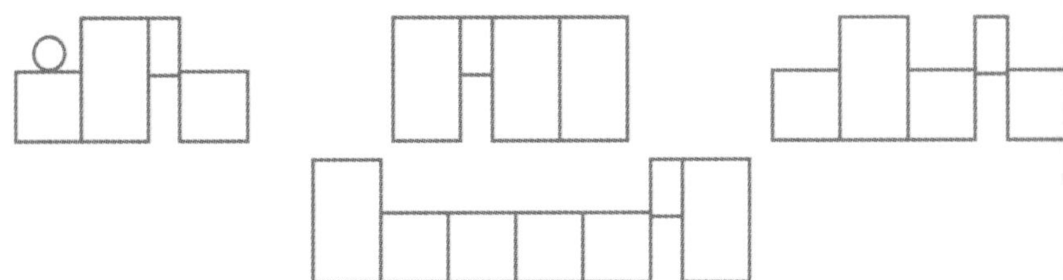

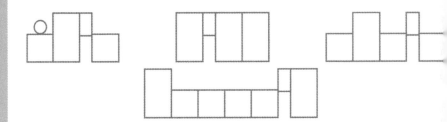

C Two Parts. Four other words have two syllables. Write them on the lines.

D Three Parts. You have one word with three syllables. Write it under its picture.

E **Definitions.** Write the list words that match these meanings.

1. coverings for the eyes ____________
2. a greeting ____________
3. a string to tie a shoe ____________
4. a large African cat ____________
5. used to call someone ____________
6. the first day of the week ____________
7. a boat with a sail ____________
8. one minus one ____________

F **Two Become One.** Match these contractions with the words they are made from. Rewrite each contraction.

I'll	have not ____________
haven't	she is ____________
she's	it is ____________
it's	I will ____________

Use two of the contractions in sentences.

____

____

____

____

G **Word Find.** Find all your list words except the contractions in the word find. You will find eleven words. You can also find color and number words.

P U R P L E F I V E S T N T
I F O U R B R O W N H W I H
N Y E L L O W Z E R O O N R
K M Y S E L F L E R E D E E
T E E B L A C K H E L L O E
T E L E P H O N E T A E R S
S A I L B O A T T E C R A E
O N D I F I V E G R E E N V
N I S O M E T I M E S E G E
E T A N W H I T E B L U E N
E I G H T S I X B O T T E N
B B E G A N O S U N D A Y S

H **Going to Church.** Sunday is the day many Christians go to church. Write about what your family does on Sunday. Try to use the words myself, sometimes, and Sunday.

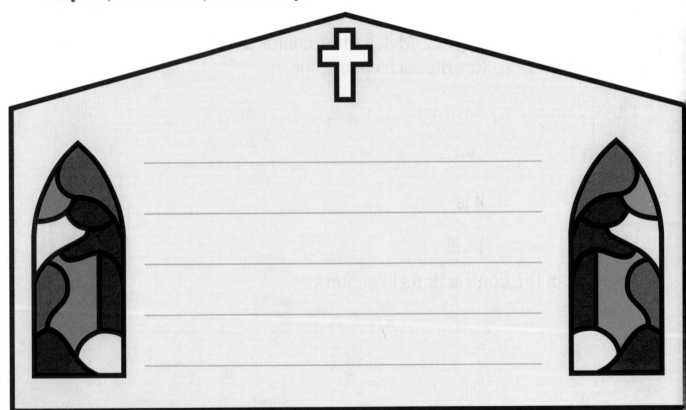

Color the telephone black if you put your Home Base Words in the Glossary this week.

Riddles. Answer each riddle and draw a picture to go with it.

1. What list word has a ring that you cannot wear?

   ____

2. What list word has the sun but could be a rainy day?

   ____

3. What list word has four letters but means nothing?

   ____

4. What list word has lids you cannot take off?

   ____

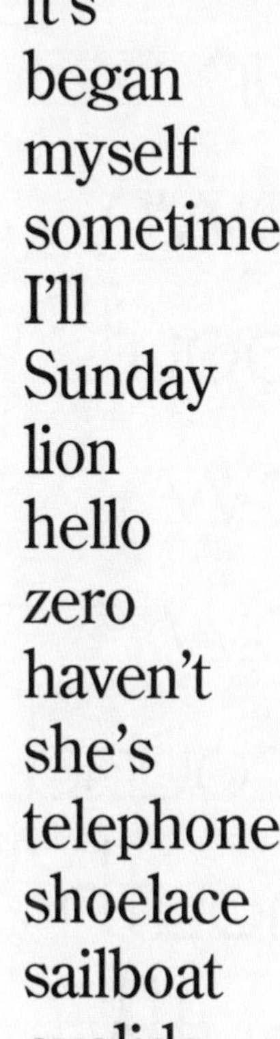

it's
began
myself
sometimes
I'll
Sunday
lion
hello
zero
haven't
she's
telephone
shoelace
sailboat
eyelids

J **Math Match.** Do these math problems. Write each answer with a word, not a number.

3 + 4	5 + 5	7 - 1	3 - 3
______	______	______	______

3 + 2	7 - 5	2 + 1	10 - 2
______	______	______	______

Robbie Robot. Put funny eyes and eyelids on Robbie.

four*
houses
out
our
down
about
how
now
around
mouth
south
mouse
towel
cowboys
flower

Target: Vowel digraphs **ou** and **ow**

A **OU and OW.** All your list words have ou or ow. Write them below in the list where they belong. Draw a shape box around each one with a red crayon and again with a blue crayon. The first one is done for you.

ou	ow
four	

B **Home Base Words.** Write your Home Base Words and draw shape boxes around them.

Color the cowboy if you put your Home Base Words in the Glossary.

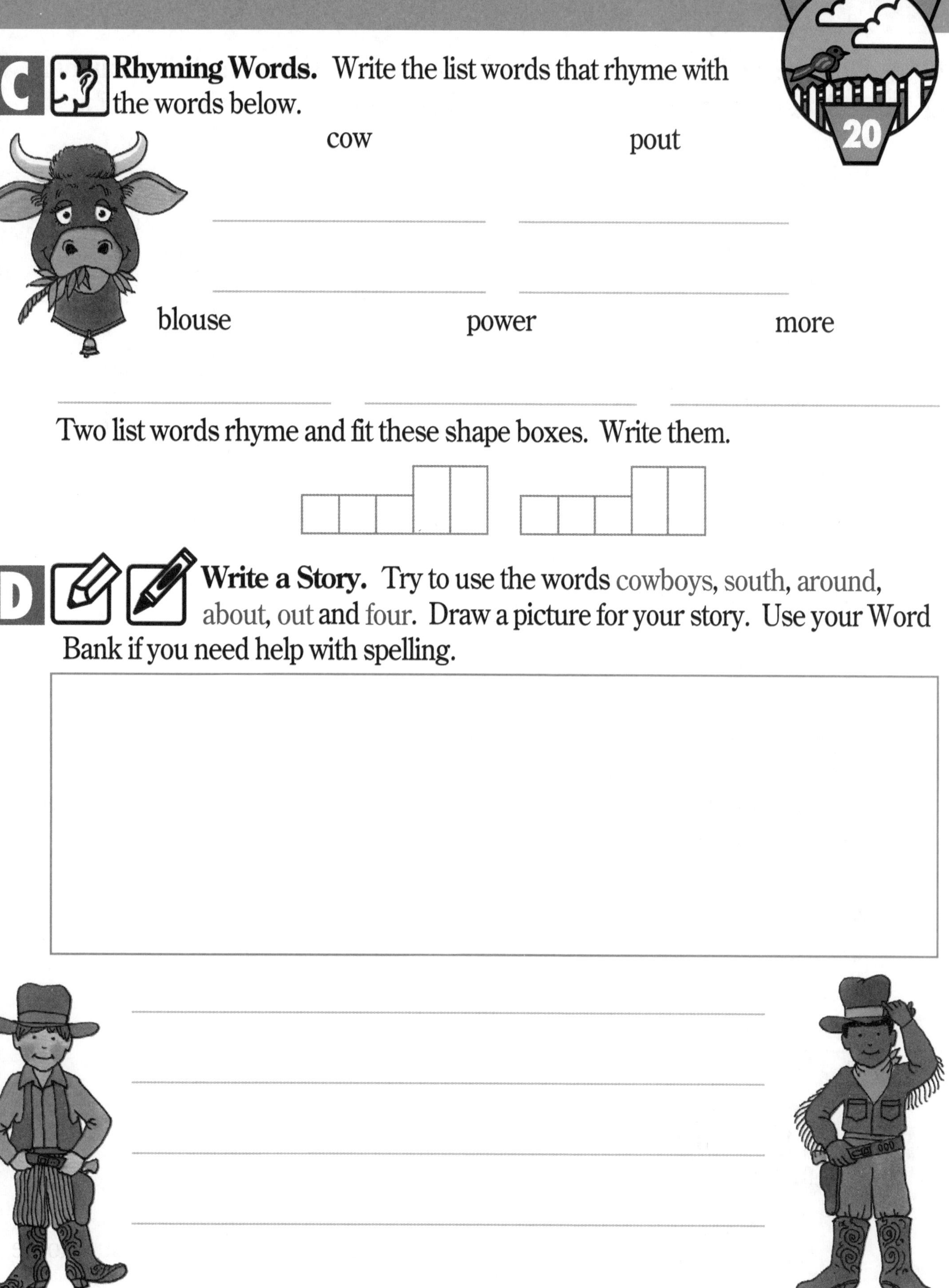

C **Rhyming Words.** Write the list words that rhyme with the words below.

cow

pout

blouse

power

more

Two list words rhyme and fit these shape boxes. Write them.

D **Write a Story.** Try to use the words cowboys, south, around, about, out and four. Draw a picture for your story. Use your Word Bank if you need help with spelling.

E **Homophones.** Our and hour are homophones. They sound alike but their spellings and meanings are different. Put them with the correct meaning.

belonging to us ____________

sixty minutes ____________

For and four are homophones. Write them in the sentences.

One less than five is ____________.

This gift is ____________ you.

Flower and flour are homophones. Match them with the correct meanings.

something to bake with ____________

the bloom of a plant ____________

F **Robbie Robot.** Put a funny mouth on Robbie. Label all the parts of his face that you know.

G **Number Names.** Write the number name for each circle.

LESSON 20

H

Words to Help or Hurt. The Bible says that your mouth is very powerful. We can bring happiness to or hurt people with words from our mouths. Use your mouth to praise the Lord and be kind to others. Copy Psalm 71:8 in your best handwriting. Draw and decorate a pretty border around the verse.

"Let my mouth be filled with Your praise
and with Your glory all the day."

____

____

____

____

four
houses
out
our
down
about
how
now
around
mouth
south
mouse
towel
cowboys
flower

I

Fill–Ins. Use list words to complete the sentences.

There are twelve ______________ on our street.

That is a sweet smelling ______________.

That town is ______________ of here.

Mother gave me a ______________ for my bath.

Tony had a ______________ as a pet.

saw
because
off
thought
brought
caught
draw
laws
aunt
awful
August
cost
awesome
jaw
soft

Target: The sound of **au** and **aw**

A **Seeing the Shape.** Write your list words in the shape boxes. Circle the letters that make the au sound with a red crayon. The spelling can be au, aw, o, augh, or ough. This same sound is often spelled a before the letter l. Draw around the shape boxes with crayons.

s a w

B **Syllable Count.** Color the box green if the word has one syllable. Color the box yellow if the word has two syllables.

awesome	thought
brought	awful
cost	August
because	caught

C **Complete the Cartoon.** Write words in the bubbles to tell the story. Try to use the words saw, off, caught, and brought. Use more list words if you can.

D **Our God is Awesome.** Did you know that awesome is a Bible word? Deuteronomy 10:17 says, "For the Lord your God is God of gods and Lord of lords, the great God, mighty and awesome." Draw a picture of something that God has made that is awesome. Write a sentence about it.

Have you put your Home Base Words in the Glossary this week? Color the moon and stars yellow if you have.

E **Meanings Match.** What list words match these meanings?

1. the opposite of on ______________________
2. captured something ______________________
3. rules for people to live by ______________________
4. your uncle's wife ______________________
5. the eighth month of the year ______________________
6. the price of something ______________________
7. the opposite of hard ______________________
8. the lower part of the face ______________________

F **Fill–Ins.** Put list words in the sentences where they belong.

1. I looked in the mirror and ______________ my face.
2. Janie came to the party ______________ she was invited.
3. I ______________ I heard my mother call me.
4. The babies ______________ their teddy bears.
5. The space shuttle looked ______________.
6. It is fun to ______________ pictures in art.
7. That fish tasted ______________.

G **Robbie Robot.** Just for fun, put some funny whiskers on Robbie's jaws.

H

Body Parts. You have spelled the names of six parts of the body. Write the word that goes with each picture.

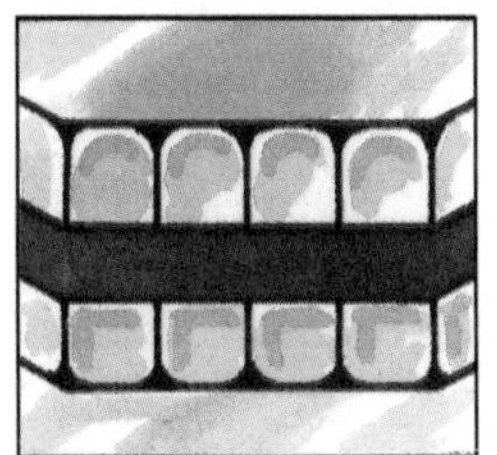

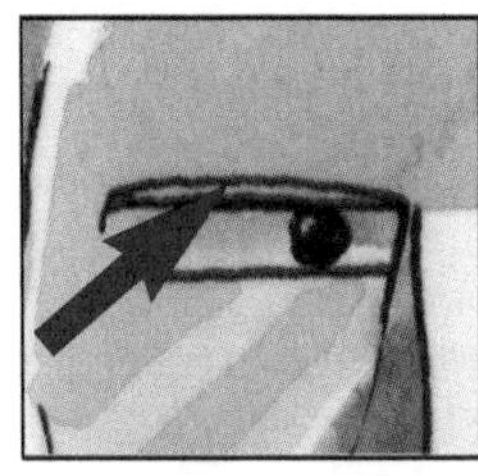

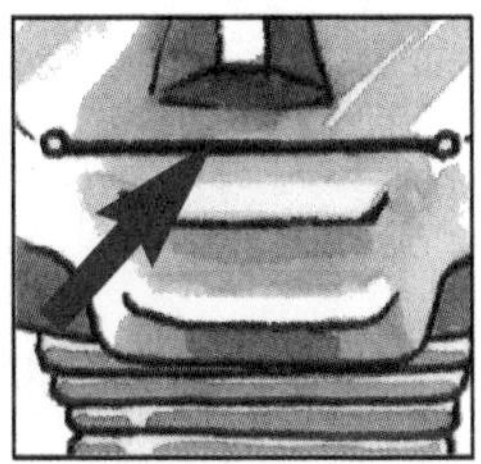

saw
because
off
thought
brought
caught
draw
laws
aunt
awful
August
cost
awesome
jaw
soft

I

August is a Fun Month. Some people go on vacation in August. Write about something you would like to do in August.

from □□
write* □□
friend □□
brown □□
glasses □□
plants □□
break □□
clothes □□
bright □□
truck □□
February □□
cross □□
price □□
dream □□
flashlight □□
□□
□□
□□

LESSON 22 Target: Blends with **l** and **r**

A **Out to Dry.** Unscramble the letters on each piece of clothing and write the word on the line. Write and draw pictures for your Home Base Words.

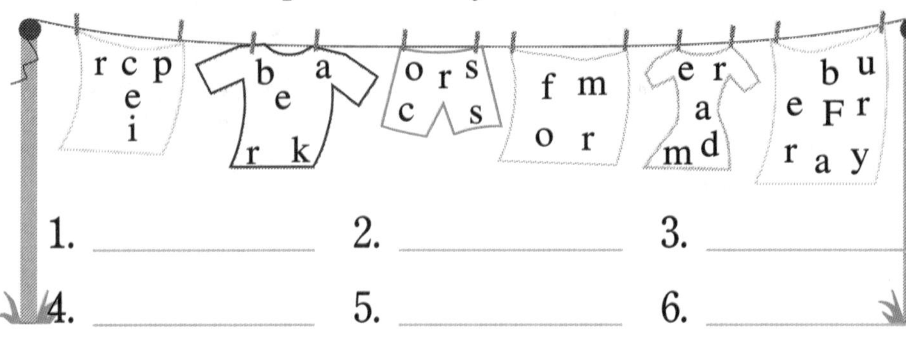

1. ______ 2. ______ 3. ______
4. ______ 5. ______ 6. ______

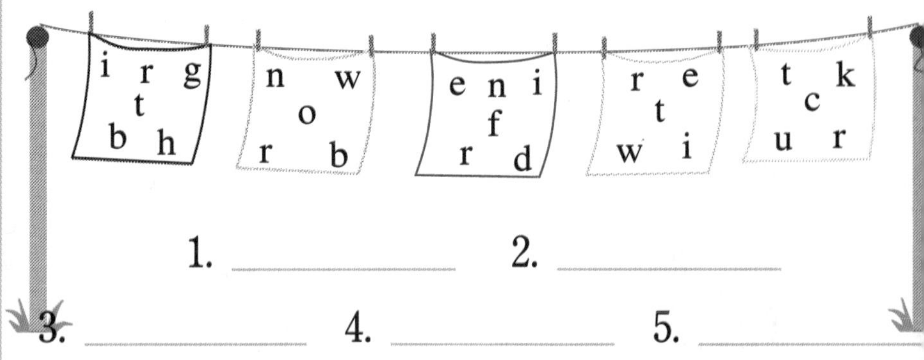

1. ______ 2. ______
3. ______ 4. ______ 5. ______

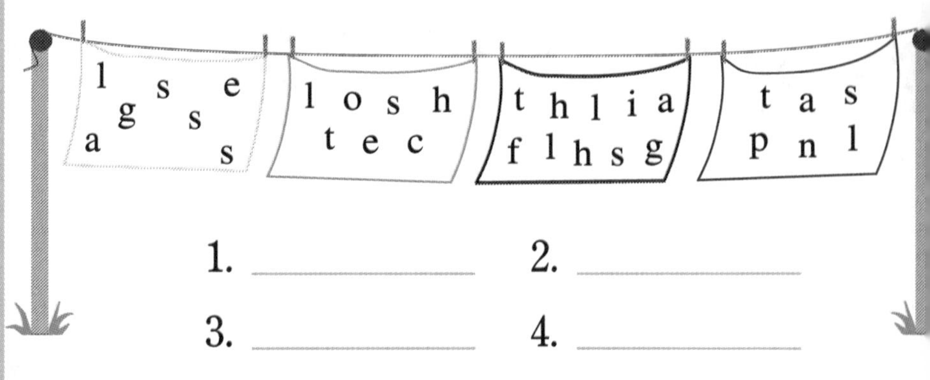

1. ______ 2. ______
3. ______ 4. ______

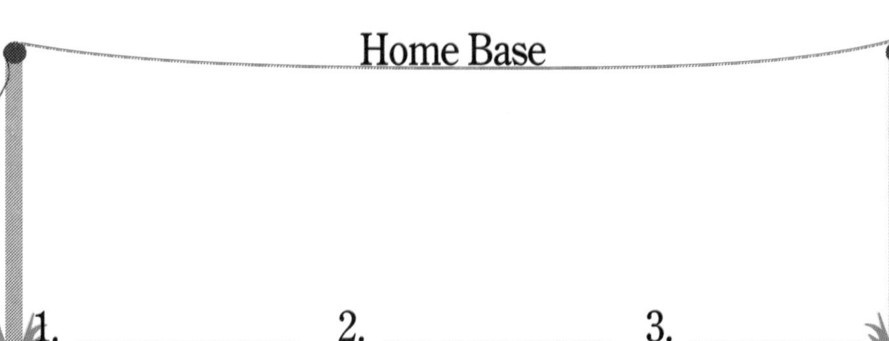

1. ______ 2. ______ 3. ______

B **Double Check.** Go back and circle the blend in each list word.

C Picture Match. Write the list word by its picture.

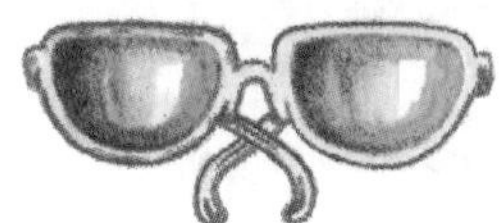

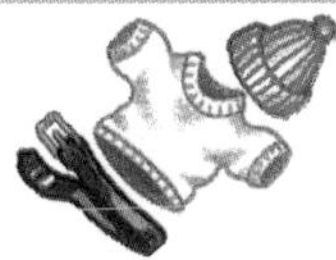

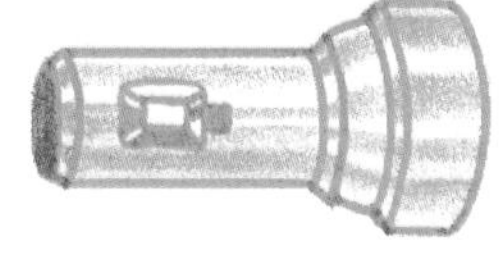

D ABC Order. Put these list words in ABC order. Sometimes you have to look at the third letter.

from friend bright
write break dream

1. ______________ 4. ______________

2. ______________ 5. ______________

3. ______________ 6. ______________

E Rhyming Words. Write the list word that rhymes. Remember that the spellings can be different.

bend ______________ sum ______________

kite ______________ seem ______________

those ______________ lake ______________

F **My Friend.** A friend is wonderful to have. Write a story about one of your friends. Tell why he or she is a good friend to you. Draw a picture of your friend.

G **Jesus, Our Friend.** The best friend we can ever have is Jesus. He loves us so much He died on the cross for our sins. Copy Proverbs 18:24b in your best handwriting. Draw and decorate a pretty border for it.

"There is a friend who sticks closer than a brother."

Have you put your Home Base Words in the Glossary this week? Color the cross brown if you have.

Word Work.

1. The word February is the name of a month. It always starts with a capital letter. Write it twice.

______ ______

2. You have a word with two meanings. You can drink from them or use them to help see. Write it twice.

______ ______

3. You have three words that mean more than one thing. Hint: They end with s. Write them.

______ ______ ______

4. One of your words begins with a silent letter. Write it twice.

______ ______

5. Write the three words that begin with a br blend. Circle the blend.

______ ______ ______

6. Write the two words that begin with an fr blend. Circle the blend.

______ ______

7. Write the word that is something you might do while you sleep.

______

8. Write the word for something father can drive.

______

9. Write the word for the cost of something.

______

10. Write the word for the place Jesus died.

______

Draw a picture of this word.

from
write
friend
brown
glasses
plants
break
clothes
bright
truck
February
cross
price
dream
flashlight

LESSON 23 Target: Blends with **s**

schools
just
snow
still
asked
slow
special
stood
speak
Spirit
stayed
swim
sheet*
rested
sticker

A **Combinations with S.** All but one of the words this week have s blended with other letters. Write your words in their shapes. Circle the s blend with a red crayon. Watch out for the word schools. It has three letters in its blend.

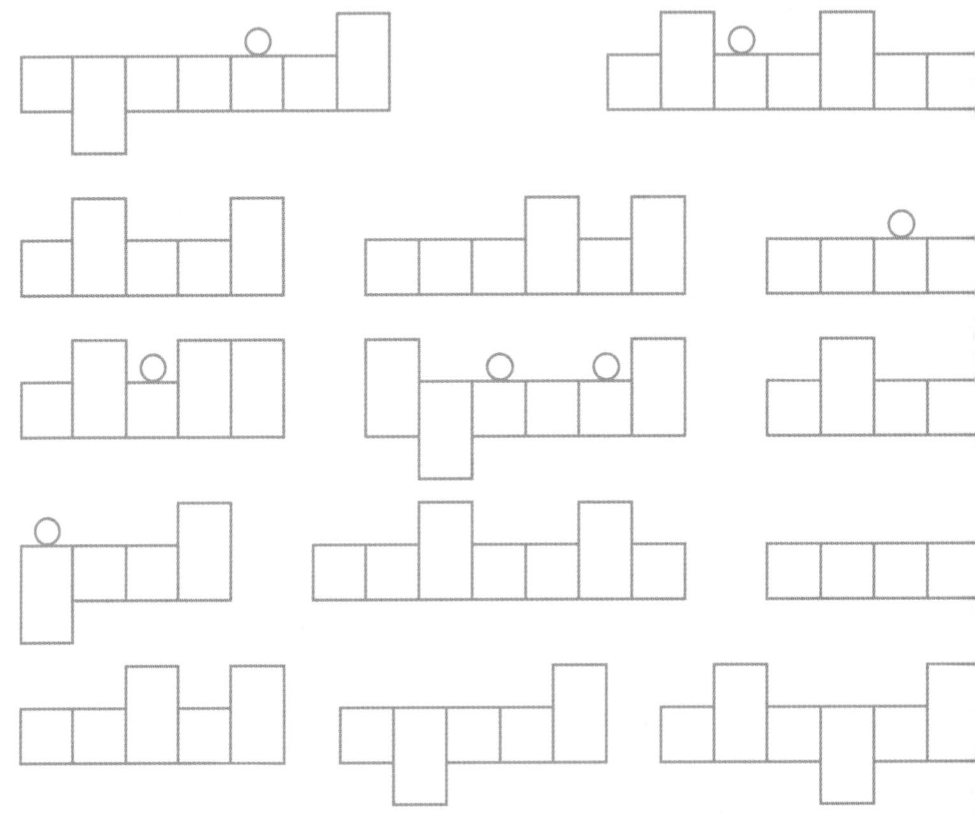

Remember sh is not a blend, but has its own sound like in shoe. Write your sh word in this silly sentence. Say it softly to your friend three times very fast.

Shy Shelly should share her

short ____________.

Color the school books blue if you put your Home Base Words in the Glossary this week.

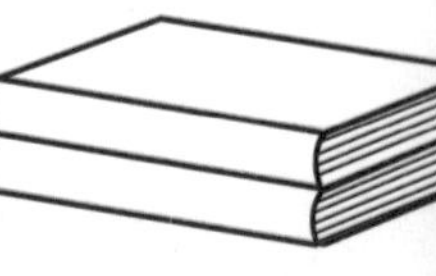

B **Crossword Puzzle.** Use your list words to complete the puzzle.

ACROSS

1. I got a _____ gift for my birthday.
2. My teacher gave me a _____ on my paper.
3. The pastor stood up to _____ at church.
4. Mike _____ me to come over to his house.
5. Students from five _____ came to the Spelling Bee.
6. The boys like to _____ in races.
7. The baby was very _____ because she was asleep.
8. We _____ up late on New Year's Eve.
9. I want _____ one scoop of ice cream, please.

DOWN

1. After the long walk, we _____.
2. The Holy _____ is our helper.
3. There was _____ on the mountain.
4. Beth _____ outside to wait for the bus.
5. The turtle in the race was _____.
6. Mother put a clean _____ on my bed.

C **Letter Spots.** Choose from the letter bank to finish these list words. Trace all the letters in each word.

a___ed
ju___
___eet
___ools
re___ed
___im

___icker
___ood
___ill
___eak
___ecial
___ow

___irit
___ayed
___ow

D **The Holy Spirit.** After Jesus went back to Heaven, God sent us the Spirit to be our helper each day. He is the One who helps us remember to do what is right. Write how the Spirit can help you today.

"He has given us of His Spirit."
I John 4:13b

E **Suffixes.** Some of your words this week have suffixes or endings that have been added to root words. Look carefully at the root word. Write your related word on the line.

ask ________ stick ________ rest ________

stay ________ school ________

F **Class Action.** Fill in the list word that fits each group.

rain, sleet, ________ Jesus, God, ________

great, super, ________ talk, say, ________

ran, walked, ________ slept, napped, ________

churches, hospitals, ________

bedspread, blanket, ________

Try some more. This time fill in an action word.

did not go ________ did not answer ________

did not work ________ did not sit ________

schools
just
snow
still
asked
slow
special
stood
speak
Spirit
stayed
swim
sheet
rested
sticker

G **Stickers.** It is fun to get a sticker. Draw one in this box.

H **Home Base Words.** Write two sentences using your Home Base Words.

____

____

____

____

schools
four
just
houses
out
our
from
saw
down
about
thought
write
friend
because
sometimes
I'll
Sunday
special

LESSON 24 Target: Review Lessons 19-23

A **Labels.** Put some of your list words with the pictures where they belong.

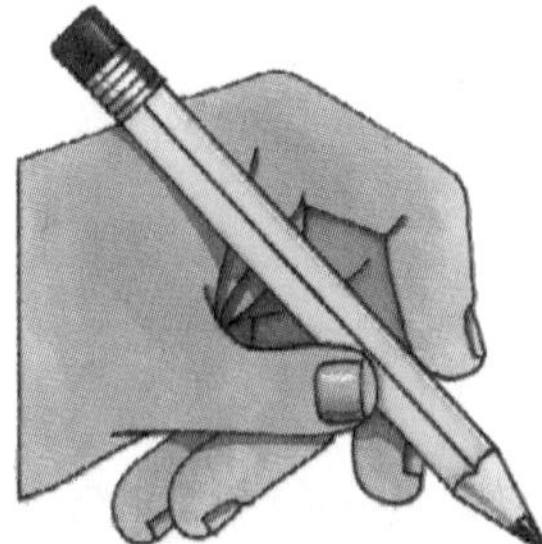

B **Special Friends.** Read Galatians 5:22 and 23. Write a sentence about how you try to be a special friend to someone.

LESSON 24

C **Vowel Digraphs.** Look at the list words. Find the words with the letters ou or ow. Write them and circle the ou or ow. Notice their sounds.

Look at the list words. Find the words with the letters au or aw. Write them and circle the au or aw.

D **Consonant Blends.** Look at the list words. Write the words with l, r or s blends in them. Circle the blends. The w in one word can be silent.

sssstttt

E **Contractions.** One of the words in the list is a contraction. Write the two words each contraction replaces; then write the contraction again.

I'll

she's

it's

F **Compound Words.** Two list words are compound words. They are made from two smaller words. Write them and circle the two words in the compound words.

G **Schools Are Special.** Write about your school. Draw a picture to go along with your story. Try to use some of your list words. Underline them.

My School

H **Fill–Ins.** Use your list words in these sentences.

1. There are two ________ on our street.
2. The cat went ________ the door.
3. Bill slid ________ the hill.
4. We will learn ________ math this year.
5. I got a card ________ my grandmother.
6. I will ________ a letter to her.
7. Mother ________ I was outside.
8. ________ are places to learn.
9. My sister is ________ years old.
10. On ________ we will go to church.
11. Can you visit ________ class?
12. ________ ask your mother if you can come.
13. We ________ an airplane in the sky.
14. I have ________ enough cake for my class.
15. ________ we have ice cream for lunch.
16. I like you ________ you are kind.
17. Be a ________ to everyone.
18. I am ________ to God.

schools
four
just
houses
out
our
from
saw
down
about
thought
write
friend
because
sometimes
I'll
Sunday
special

I **Word Search.** Circle with red the list words that are hidden in this puzzle.

specialla wsoutawesomethoughtcostfriend
brownwritespecialcrossbecausestillI'll
schoolssnowdrawcaughtsometimesSundayat
sailboateyelidsmouthdownsawfromlawsoff
softhousesglassesourawfulaboutjustfour

All the other letters make words from lessons you have had before. Circle all the other words you can find with blue.

something
bring
coming
going
along
nothing
getting
strong
spring
swing
saying
hung
reading
sang
pushing

LESSON 25 Target: Words with **ng** and **ing**

A **Adding ING.** Change the order of the letters in each box and add ing to make a list word.

shetom	rb	ocm

og	thon	tegt

prs	ws	ays

rade	suph

Now add ng to this group.

loa	rots

uh	sa

LESSON 25

B

Roots. Write the root words for these words. Write the list word that is related to each root word. Circle the root word in the list word. The first one is done for you.

goes	go	going
gets		
reads		
pushed		
says		
comes		

Remember to drop the e to add ing to come.

C

Best Fit. Choose a list word that best fits each sentence.

1. The ________ man lifted the heavy box.
2. He ________ a nice song.
3. It is warm in the ________.
4. We have a new ________ on the playground.
5. Mother ________ the shirt up to dry.
6. Please ________ cookies to the party.
7. There was ________ in the mailbox.

D

Compound Words. Write the two smaller words and the list words on the lines.

s________ + t________ = ________

________ + l________ = ________

E **Strong in the Lord.** The Bible says, "Be strong in the Lord and in the power of His might." That means the Lord will help us to do what He wants us to do. How are you being strong in the Lord today?

F **Glossary Glance.** Look in the Glossary for these words. Write the page number where each one is found. Read the definition and sentence. Write a new sentence for each word.

Word	Page	Sentence
1. reading	____	____________
2. spring	____	____________
3. swing	____	____________
4. sang	____	____________
5. strong	____	____________

If you put your Home Base Words in the Glossary this week, color the birds blue.

something
bring
coming
going
along
nothing
getting
strong
spring
swing
saying
hung
reading
sang
pushing

Spring Time. Finish drawing the spring picture. Write a story about your picture. Try to use some list words and Home Base Words in your story.

went
wants
don't
front
drink
can't
pink
spend
print
jumped
climbed*
thumb*
thank you
repent
thinking

LESSON 26 Target: Final blends

A **Word Shapes.** Write the words in the boxes where they belong. Trace the outlines of the words carefully with two different colors.

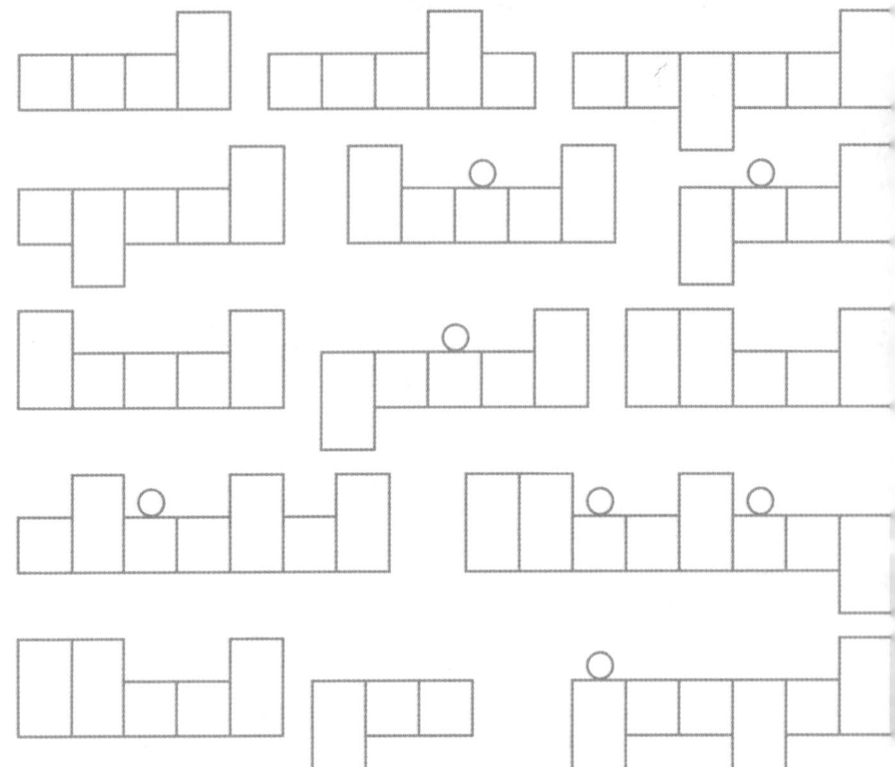

B **Contractions.** Write the two contractions in the boxes and match them with the words they replace. Remember that an apostrophe stands for a missing letter.

do not

can not

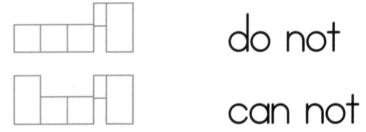

C **Silent Letters.** Two words have a silent b after an m. Use them in these sentences.

1. The monkey ______________ the tree.

2. I hurt my ______________.

D **ABC Order.** Write your Home Base Words in ABC order.

E **Pink Is a Fun Color.** Draw three pink things and write a sentence about each picture.

F **I'm Sorry.** Repent means to be so sorry about something that we stop doing it. Look up Matthew 3:2 in your Bible and write it on the lines. Think about the verse as you write.

If you have put your Home Base Words in the Glossary this week, color the hearts pink.

G **Crazy Sentences.** The words in these sentences are all mixed-up. Can you fix them and write them on the lines?

1. pink a Beth drink wants

2. jumped climbed Chris and the playground on

3. to Mom me say wants "Thank you"

4. print on said name Miss Chase to front my the

5. all now want I money don't to my spend

Robbie Robot. Robbie put his thumbprint all over the page. Draw something with each thumbprint.

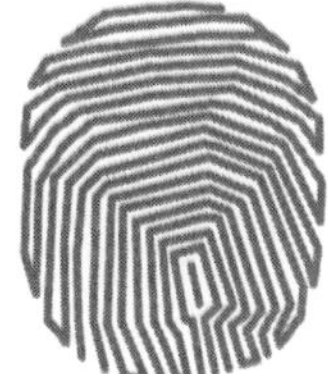

went
wants
don't
front
drink
can't
pink
spend
print
jumped
climbed
thumb
thank you
repent
thinking

I

Definitions. Write your words under their meanings.

a color	do not	went up a tree
not back	swallow water	cannot
use money	desires	studying

Thank–You Notes. We should always thank people who help us. On another sheet of paper, write a thank–you note to your teacher, principal or parents.

left □□
found □□
built □□
mind □□
children □□
cold □□
felt □□
himself □□
milk □□
walked* □□
mild □□
salt □□
blind □□
billfold □□
salvation* □□
□□
□□
□□

LESSON 27 Target: More final blends

A **Word Sort.** Write your list words on the milk carton where they belong.

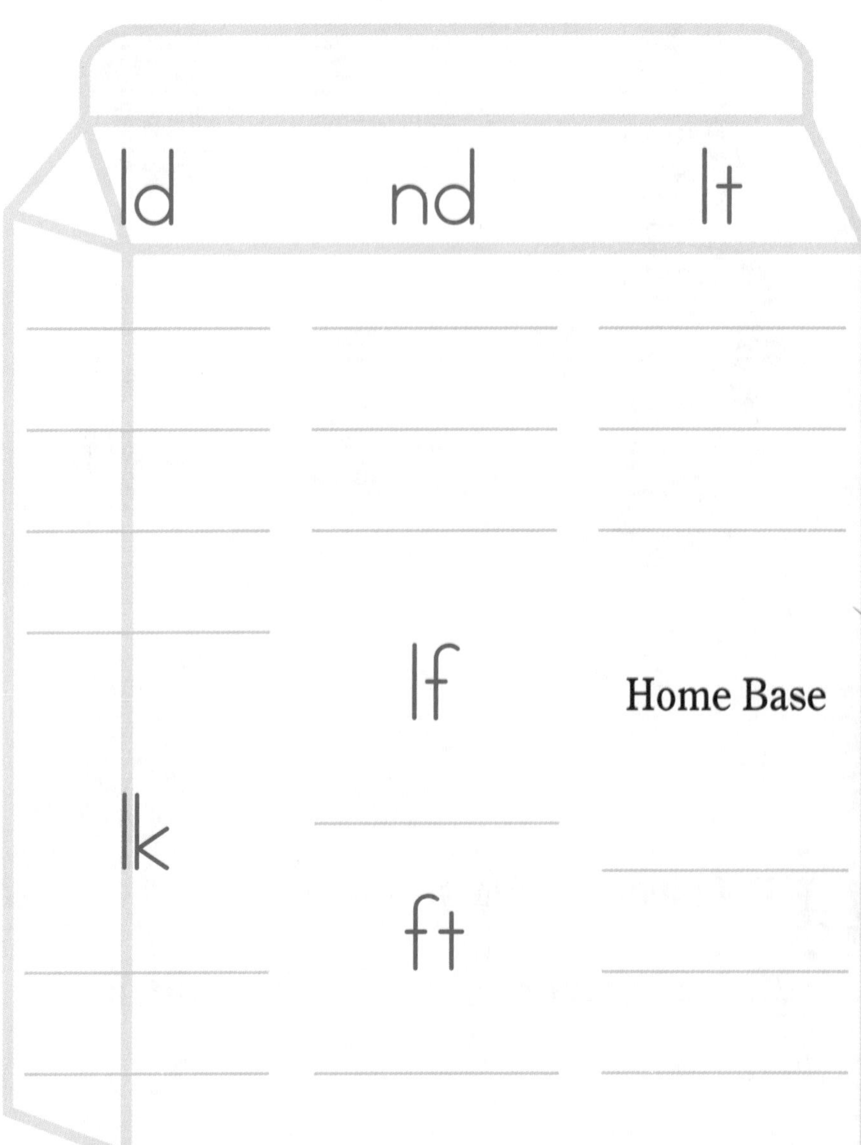

B **Letter Check.** Look at the blends in the salt shaker. Go back and circle them in the words you wrote.

Word Find. Find all of your list words in the puzzle. Also you can find number words and colors spelled backwards. See how many you can find.

```
d e r s s a l v a t i o n e e r g
e n z n w o l l e y v n e v e l e
v i e c h i l d r e n b z i o w t
i n u x b n e v e s r u o f h a n
f e l t l y c o l d p i r m i l d
x t b z i f t h g i e l m i l k e
i p l e n o n e l e f t k l g e e
s a l t d u f b i l l f o l d d r
u j o m i n d o h i m s e l f i h
k c a l b d n w o r b e v l e w t
```

D Meanings.

1. What are young people called? ________
2. What word means not lost? ________
3. What is a person who cannot see? ________
4. What is the opposite of right? ________
5. What drink comes from a cow? ________
6. What goes with pepper? ________
7. What can hold money? ________

E Mixed–Up Syllables. Can you make these syllables into four list words?

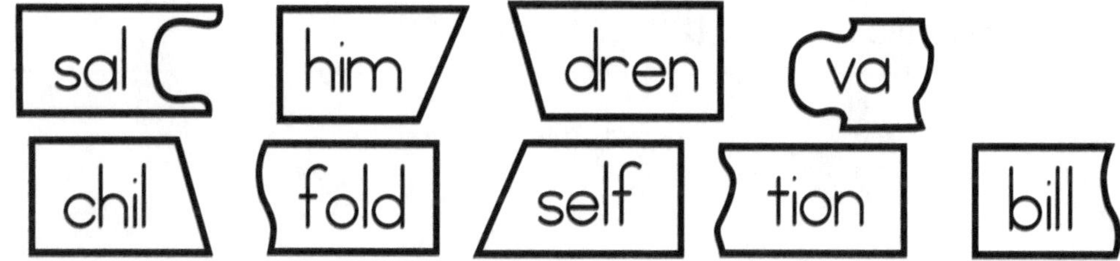

________ ________

________ ________

F **Heavenly Home.** The Bible says, "Our God is the God of salvation." Jesus died to save us. Because He died, we can go to Heaven with Him. Answer each question with a complete sentence.

Can children go to Heaven?

____

Will people be blind or cold in Heaven?

____

Who built the pearly gates in Heaven?

____

____

Must you have salvation to go to Heaven?

____

____

Must every person accept Jesus himself or herself?

____

____

Have you found salvation?

____

Draw a picture of some things in Heaven.

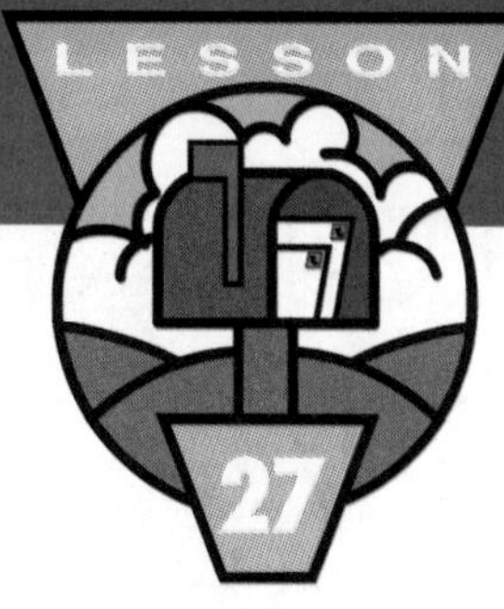

left
found
built
mind
children
cold
felt
himself
milk
walked
mild
salt
blind
billfold
salvation

Change Places. These letters make two list words. Write them here.

Now write two sentences using these words.

Rhyming Words. Write a list word that rhymes with each word below.

talked	child	kind	round
silk	fold	knelt	tilt
fault	will hold	vacation	find

Home Base Words. Write two of your Home Base Words in sentences.

Color the children's clothes if you put your Home Base Words in the Glossary this week.

many

any

pretty

very

only

every

happy

money

body

July

puppy

sorry

candy

cookies *

Holy

LESSON 28 Target: Last syllable y

A **Word Shapes.** Write the list words on the cookie jar in their shape boxes.

B **Capitals.** Two words in the list this week begin with capitals. Write them by their meanings.

the seventh month ____________

belonging to or coming from God ____________

C **Rebus Puzzles.** Use the picture clues to find out what the list word is.

+ dy = ____________

+ ies = ____________

+ y = ____________

mo + = ____________

+ y = ____________

Poor Timmy. Use nine of your words in this story. Finish the last part of the story.

One day in J _ _ _ _, Timmy was v _ _ _ _ hungry. He went to the bakery where he saw m _ _ _ _ c _ _ _ _ _ _ _ _ _, p _ _ _ _ _ cakes, pies, and some c _ _ _ _ _ _. He was s _ _ _ _ _ that he didn't have a _ _ m _ _ _ _ _. Poor Timmy! Maybe the baker will ____

____

If you put your Home Base Words in the Glossary this week, color the puppy brown.

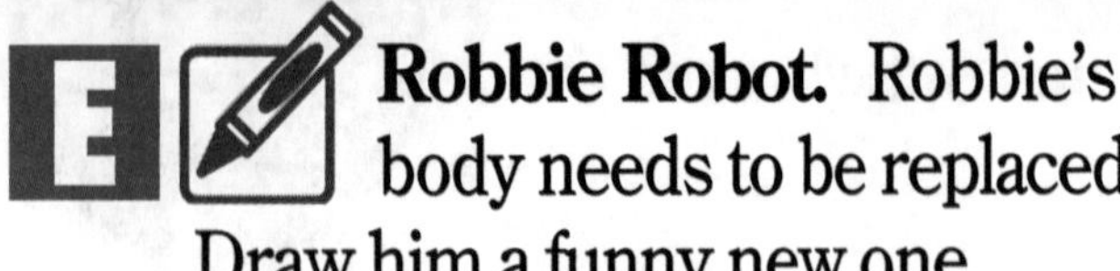

E **Robbie Robot.** Robbie's body needs to be replaced. Draw him a funny new one. Label the parts that you draw.

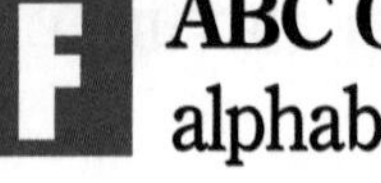

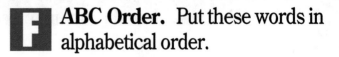

F **ABC Order.** Put these words in alphabetical order.

sorry pretty puppy
only very any

G **Happiness Is. . . .** What makes you happy? Write about three things that make you happy.

H **God Is Holy.** He is very great. He is awesome. He is powerful. Look up Isaiah 6:3 and write the verse in your best handwriting. Draw a pretty border for it.

____

____

____

____

many
any
pretty
very
only
every
happy
money
body
July
puppy
sorry
candy
cookies
Holy

I **Categories.** Fill in the word that fits in the same category as the two words listed.

1. May, June, ________________
2. all, several, ________________
3. quarters, dollars, ________________
4. kitten, calf, ________________
5. repent, apology, ________________
6. beautiful, handsome, ________________
7. chest, back, ________________
8. some, a little, ________________

J **Syllables.** Write these words. Put a line between the syllables. Look in the Glossary if you need help.

very	body	candy	happy
puppy	pretty	sorry	many

____________________ ____________________

____________________ ____________________

____________________ ____________________

____________________ ____________________

little
people
apple
middle
simple
purple
puzzles
puddle
ankle
bicycle
Bible
uncle's
giggles
buckle
tickles

LESSON 29 Target: Last syllable **le**

A **Parts of a Puzzle.** Write the list words on the puzzle pieces. Be sure to match your words to the letters and blanks that have been written for you. Write your Home Base Words on the extra pieces.

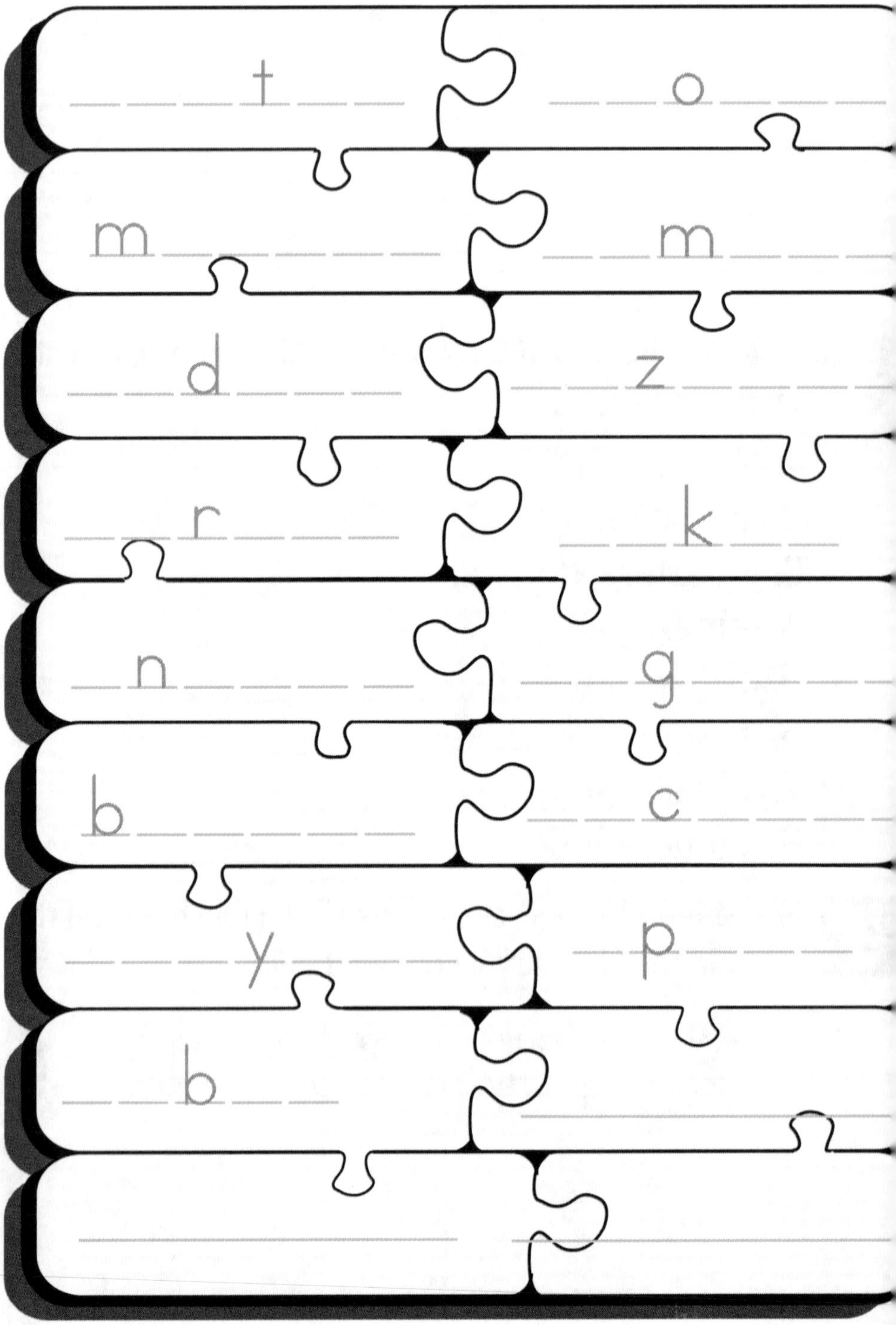

__ __ t __ __   __ __ o __ __ __

m __ __ __ __ __   __ __ m __ __ __

__ __ d __ __ __   __ __ z __ __ __ __

__ __ r __ __ __   __ __ k __ __

__ n __ __ __ __   __ __ g __ __ __ __

b __ __ __ __ __ __   __ __ c __ __ __

__ __ y __ __ __ __   __ p __ __ __ __

__ __ b __ __   ______

______   ______

Color the puzzle pieces brown if you put your Home Base Words in the Glossary.

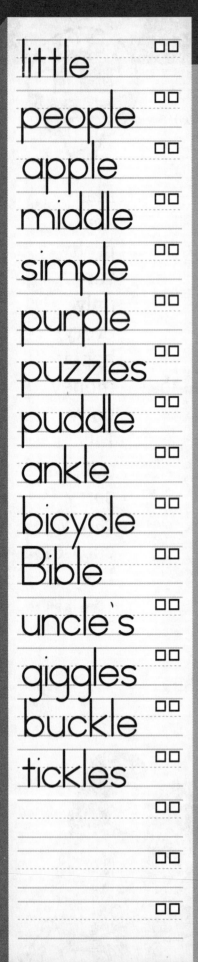

B Picture Match. Write the word that goes with the picture.

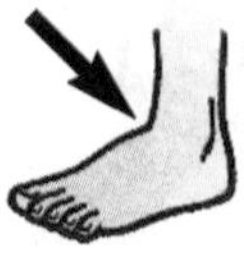

C The Bible Is the Word of God.

It helps to lead us just like a light. It helps us to know the right way. Look up Psalm 119:105 and write the verse. Make a beautiful border around it.

D **Crossword Puzzle.** Use all of your list words in this puzzle.

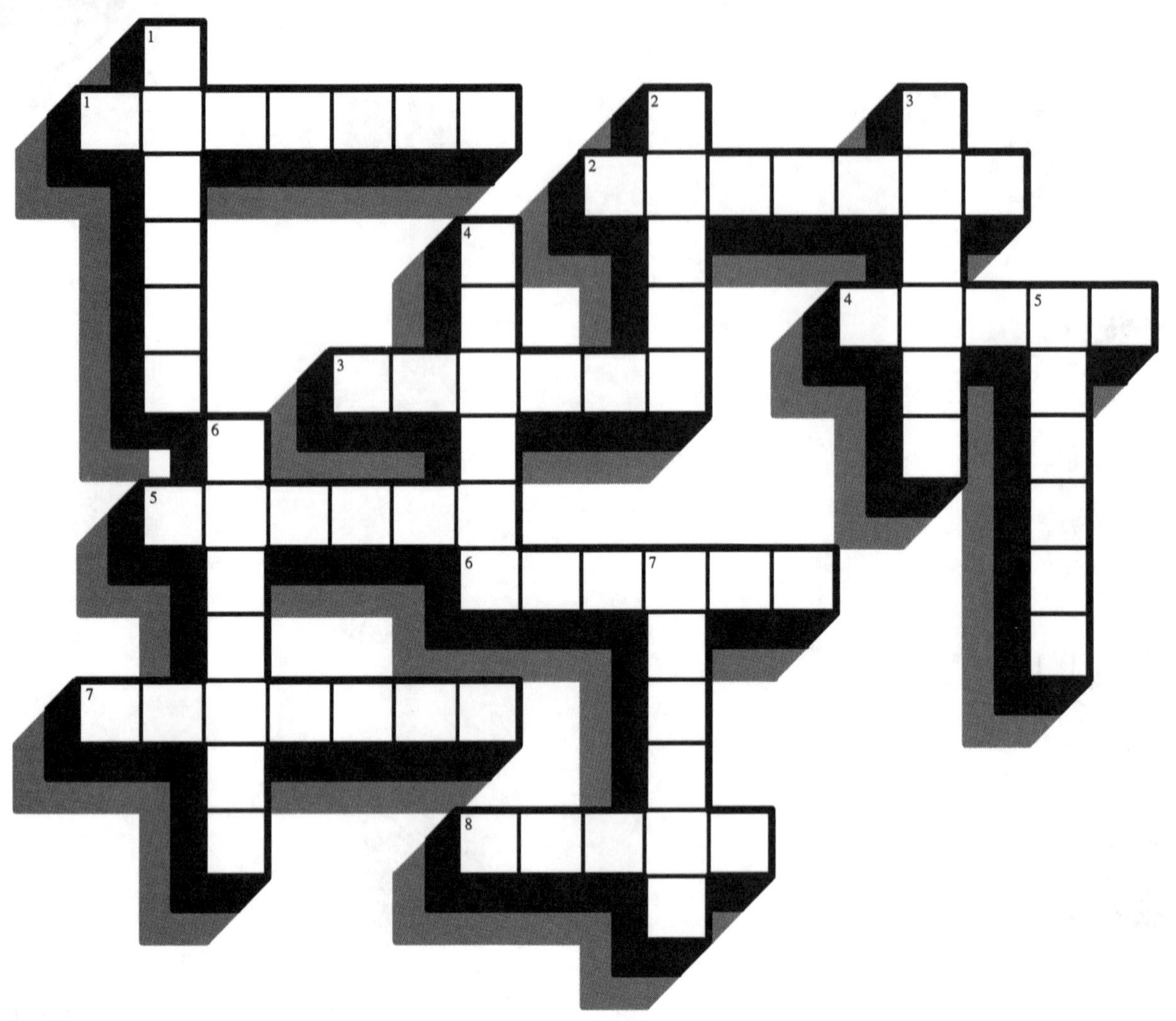

Across

1. The pieces to the ____ were all mixed-up.
2. Meg ____ at the cartoons.
3. The ____ on my belt is broken.
4. The shiny, red ____ was delicious.
5. Mike was in the ___ of the picture.
6. The math work was ____.
7. My grandpa ____ me and makes me laugh.
8. Jim twisted his ____ in the ball game.

Down

1. The mud ____ was in the street.
2. The ____ is the Word of God.
3. There are four ____ in my family.
4. My ____ name is Steven.
5. I just want a ____ piece of pizza.
6. I rode my ____ to the store.
7. The ____ dress is Jessica's favorite.

E Story Time. Use these words in the story.

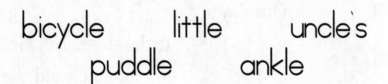

bicycle little uncle's
puddle ankle

One day Tony borrowed his ______________

______________. He rode it through a ______________.

The water came up to his

______________. A ______________

boy saw him. He thought Tony

should be more careful.

little
people
apple
middle
simple
purple
puzzles
puddle
ankle
bicycle
Bible
uncle's
giggles
buckle
tickles

F Circle Puzzles. Do these simple little puzzles. Start on the outside and circle your list words. Make a circle puzzle with your Home Base Words. Have a friend circle the words.

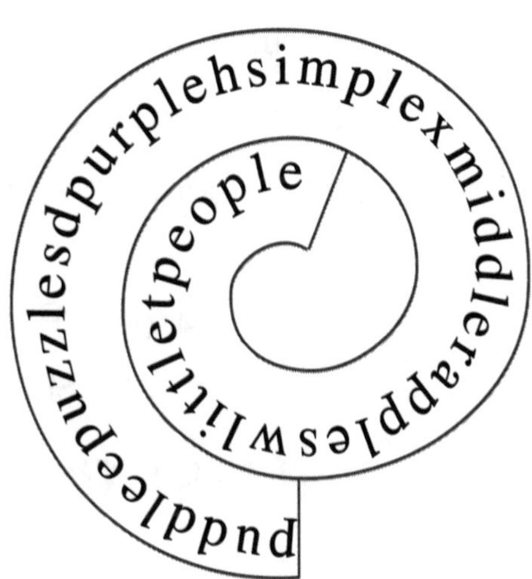

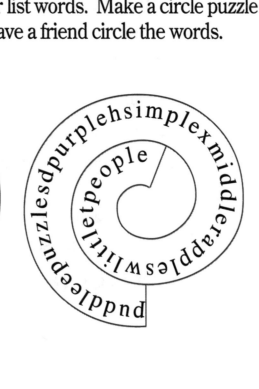

Friend's Name: ______________________

went
little
wants
any
don't
people
pretty
front
found
only
every
built
going
something
coming
very
Bible
nothing

A **Cakes and More Cakes.** Use the list words in the story where they belong.

One day a ___ ___ ___ t ___ ___ girl was ___ ___ i ___ ___ to the store. Her Grandma was ___ ___ m ___ ___ ___ for lunch and she wanted to buy ___ ___ ___ ___ t h ___ ___ ___ special to eat.

First she saw a ___ r ___ ___ ___ ___ cake in the ___ ___ ___ ___ t of the store. Then she ___ ___ n ___ to the back of the store. She ___ ___ ___ ___ ___ ___ ___ n ___ more cakes. ___ v ___ ___ ___ shelf was ___ ___ r ___ full of cakes! She asked the storekeeper, "___ ___ ___ ___ ___ ___ o ___ ___ ___ eat ___ n ___ food but cake?"

He said, "N ___ ___ ___ ___ ___ ___ but cake! Everyone ___ ___ ___ ___ s cake!"

The little girl went home and ___ ___ i ___ ___ her Grandma a ___ ___ b ___ ___ holder. Her Grandma was very pleased. Sometimes things we make are better than the things we buy!

B **Question.** Put the words in the right order to make a question.

people Are coming any to little see the puppies?

C **Syllable Check.** Write your list words in the boxes where they belong. Check your Glossary if you need help.

One Syllable	Two Syllables Final ing	More Than One Syllable Final y

Two Syllables Final le

ing le y

God's Word. Look up Psalm 119:11 in your Bible and write it in your best handwriting. Draw a pretty border for the verse.

E **ABC Order.** Write the words in each box in alphabetical order.

people little wants any	pretty something coming found	very built going Bible

F **Glossary Glance.** Look up these words in the Glossary. Write the sentence that is used for each word or write a sentence of your own.

1. went ______

2. don't ______

3. front ______

4. only ______

5. every ______

6. nothing ______

G **Silly Sentences.** You can use the letters in a word to write something silly. Look at any. If you use each letter as the first letter of a word you could write this: Ants need yards.

Here is another one. Look at very. Vincent eats ripe yams. Now you try it. Use the next four words to write something silly.

1. went ______________________________

____

2. don't ______________________________

____

3. built ______________________________

____

4. front ______________________________

____

went
little
wants
any
don't
people
pretty
front
found
only
every
built
going
something
coming
very
Bible
nothing

H **Putting It Together.** Here are some mixed-up syllables. Put them together to make seven of your list words.

pret	ing	an	ing	go	ple	noth
com	ty	some	y	peo	ing	thing

______________________ ______________________

______________________ ______________________

______________________ ______________________

____

hard
horses
morning
start
parking
important
party
March
garden
north
working
orange
arms
forgive
Lord

LESSON 31 Target: Words with **ar** and **or**

A **A Garden of Words.** Write the list words in the garden. Draw a box around each one with an orange crayon. Write your Home Base Words, too. Put a box around them.

ar

or

Home Base

Color the pumpkins orange if you put your Home Bas Words in the Glossary.

B **Robbie Robot.** Robbie's arms need ome repairs. Fix them for him. Vrite arms. ______

C **Syllable Soup.** These syllables got all mixed-up. Put them in the right order and write list words on the lines.

ty park work gar ing ange
morn den par for ing or
im ing tant give por

______ ______

______ ______

______ ______

______ ______

D **A Garden Is Fun.** Write directions for someone who wants to start a garden. Try to use these words.

hard start important garden working

. ______

. ______

. ______

. ______

. ______

E **Sentence Sense.** Use some of these words to complete the sentences.

park	March	worked	forgive
parking	marched	work	forgiveness
parks	march	working	forgiving

1. Strong winds blow in the month of ______________.
2. We were ______________ hard on our lessons.
3. Beth and Mike played in the ______________.
4. Will you ______________ in the parade?
5. Dad was ______________ our car.
6. You got 100% on your school ______________.
7. Will you ______________ me for my mistake?
8. Thank you for ______________ me. I feel better.

F **An Acrostic.** Write the words that fit on each line. The letters in the boxes will make the answer to the riddle below.

1. means a lot to you __ [ ] __ __ __ __ __ __ __
2. doing our work __ [ ] __ __ __ __ __
3. animals to ride __ __ [ ] __ __ __
4. __ __ __ __ __ [ ] a place to grow plants
5. __ __ __ __ [ ] __ __ to not hold a grudge
6. opposite of south [ ] __ __ __ __
7. __ __ __ __ __ __ [ ] putting a car in a space

Riddle: What comes every day and makes Lazy Lester get up?

__ __ __ __ __ __ __

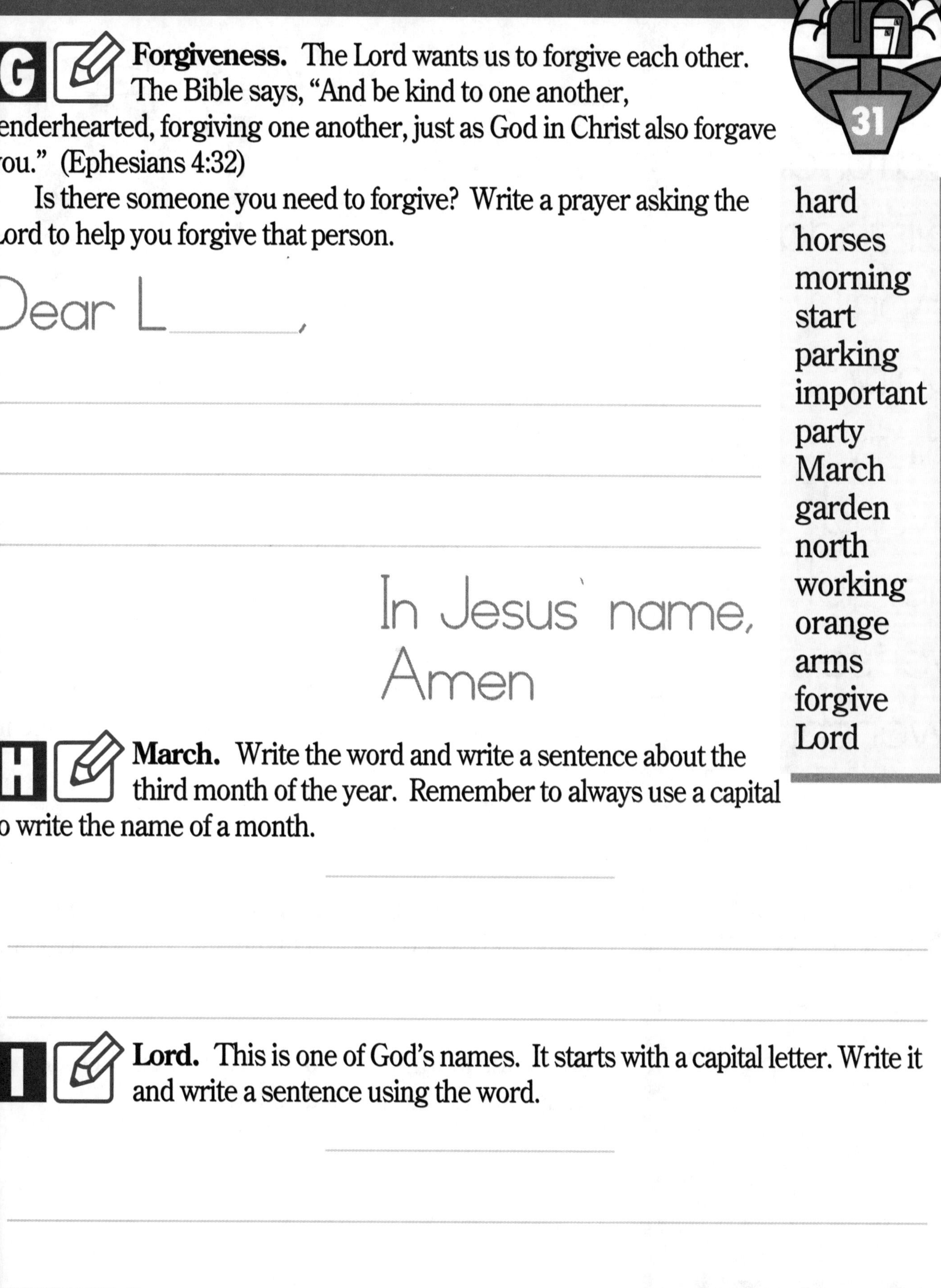

LESSON 31

G **Forgiveness.** The Lord wants us to forgive each other. The Bible says, "And be kind to one another, enderhearted, forgiving one another, just as God in Christ also forgave ʻou." (Ephesians 4:32)

Is there someone you need to forgive? Write a prayer asking the ʟord to help you forgive that person.

Dear L_____,

In Jesus' name,
Amen

hard
horses
morning
start
parking
important
party
March
garden
north
working
orange
arms
forgive
Lord

H **March.** Write the word and write a sentence about the third month of the year. Remember to always use a capital o write the name of a month.

I **Lord.** This is one of God's names. It starts with a capital letter. Write it and write a sentence using the word.

were
turn
Saturday
birthday
April*
color
dirty
word
herself
verse
worship
girl's
third
miracle*
hurting

LESSON 32 Target: Words with **er**, **ir**, **or** and **ur**

A Work with Words.

1. Three words have an er in them. Write them and circle the er.

2. Three words have ur in them. Write them and circle the ur.

3. Three words have or in them. Write them and circle the or.

4. Write all the words that have ir except miracle. These four words have the same sound. Circle the ir

5. Now write the word twice that means "something only God can do." Listen to the different sound of ir.

6. Write the fourth month of the year twice. Remember that it always has a capital letter.

7. Write your Home Base Words.

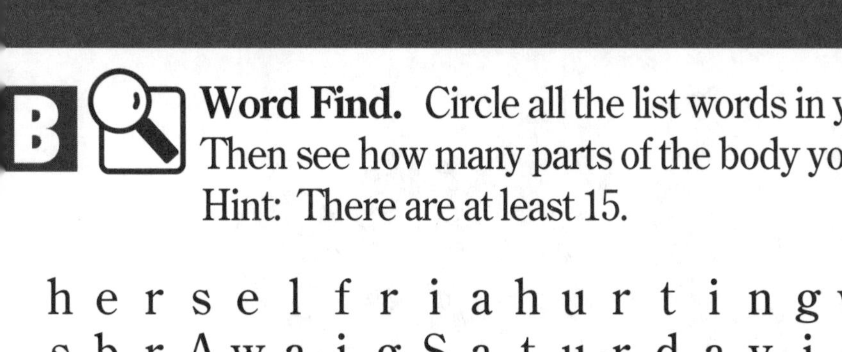

B **Word Find.** Circle all the list words in your puzzle. Then see how many parts of the body you can find. Hint: There are at least 15.

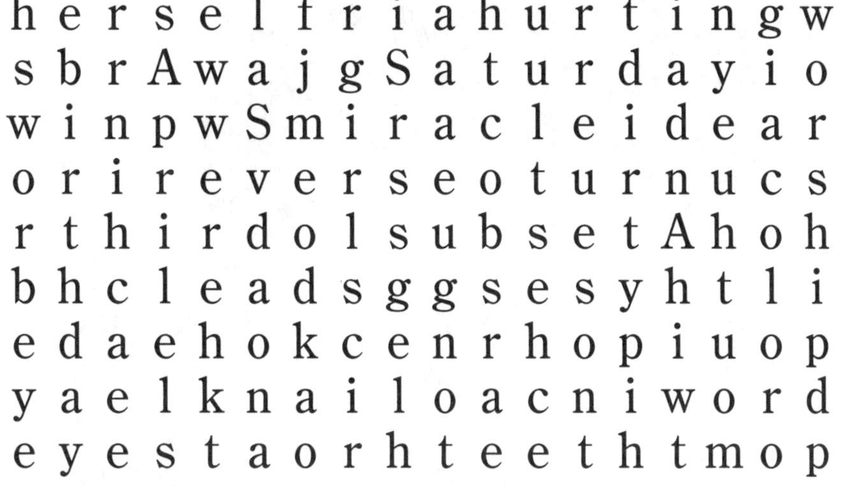

h e r s e l f r i a h u r t i n g w
s b r A w a j g S a t u r d a y i o
w i n p w S m i r a c l e i d e a r
o r i r e v e r s e o t u r n u c s
r t h i r d o l s u b s e t A h o h
b h c l e a d s g g s e s y h t l i
e d a e h o k c e n r h o p i u o p
y a e l k n a i l o a c n i w o r d
e y e s t a o r h t e e t h t m o p

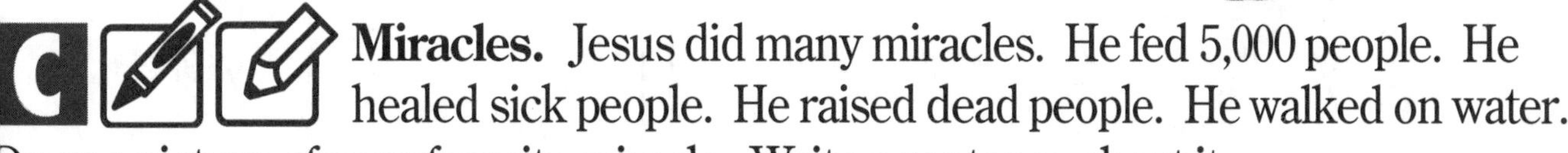

C **Miracles.** Jesus did many miracles. He fed 5,000 people. He healed sick people. He raised dead people. He walked on water. Draw a picture of your favorite miracle. Write a sentence about it.

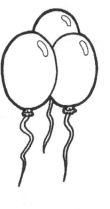

Choose any colors for these birthday balloons if you entered your Home Base Words in the Glossary.

D **Birthday Party.** Write a story about this picture. Use some of these words in your story. Try to use some of your Home Base Words, too.

Saturday	April	herself	turn
birthday	color	girl's	were

E **Meanings Match.** Match the list words with their meanings.

the seventh day of the week	the opposite of clean	to honor God
one part of a song	the day you were born	to change directions

F **Girl's or Girls.** The word girls means more than one girl. The word girl's means something that belongs to a girl. Write a sentence about a girl's kitten.

were
turn
Saturday
birthday
April
color
dirty
word
herself
verse
worship
girl's
third
miracle
hurting

G **Fill–Ins.** Use some list words in the sentences where they belong.

1. My favorite ______________ is orange.
2. I missed one ______________ on the spelling test.
3. It was a ______________ when Jesus healed the blind man.
4. My thumb has been ______________ since I fell yesterday.
5. I will be in ______________ grade next year.
6. There ______________ six fish in the bowl.
7. She saw ______________ in the mirror.

H **Home Base Words.** Choose one of your Home Base Words and write its meaning in your own words.

Word: ______________________________

Meaning: ______________________________

over
after
better
father
water
another
brother
summer
under
teacher
dinner
winter
number
finger
master

LESSON 33 Target: Last syllable **er**

A **Seeing the Shape.** Write the list words on the teacher's board. Circle the er in each word with a color.

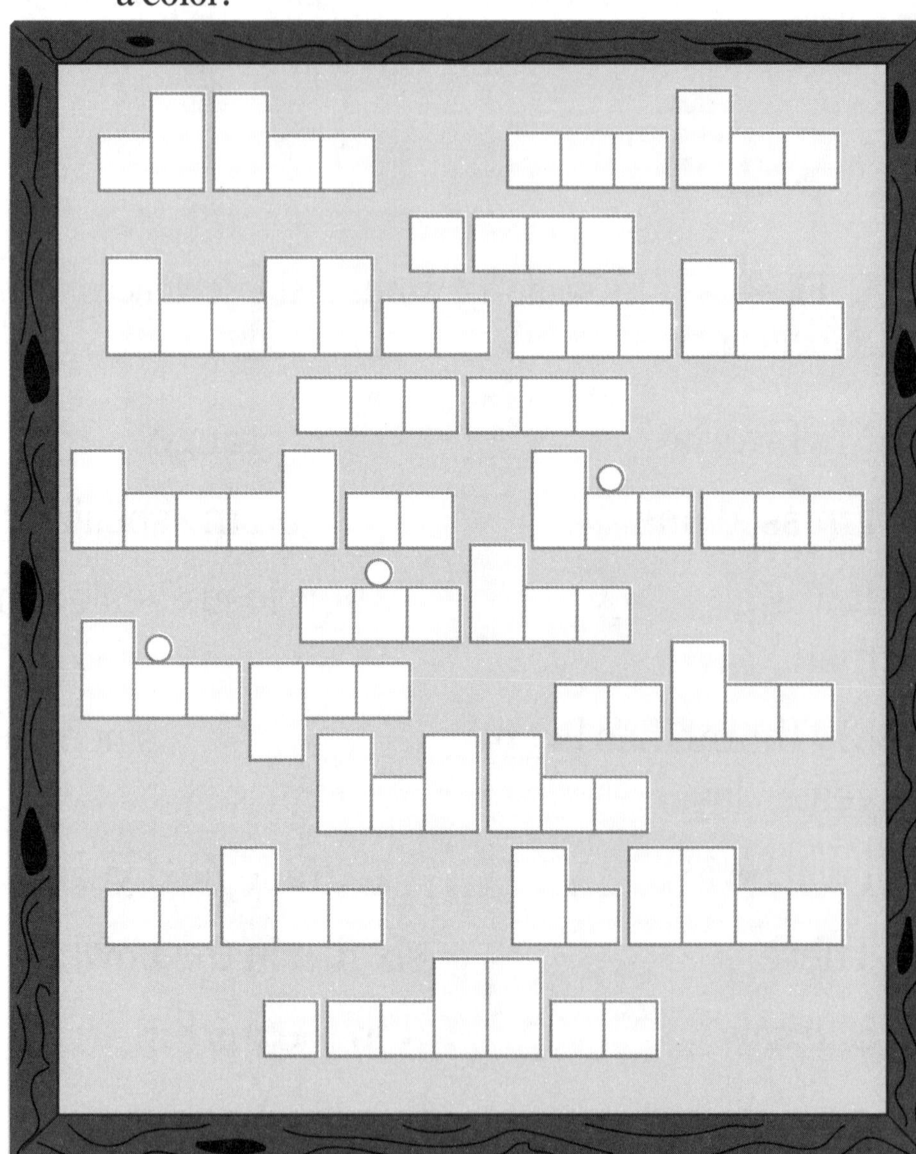

Write your Home Base Words on the erasers.

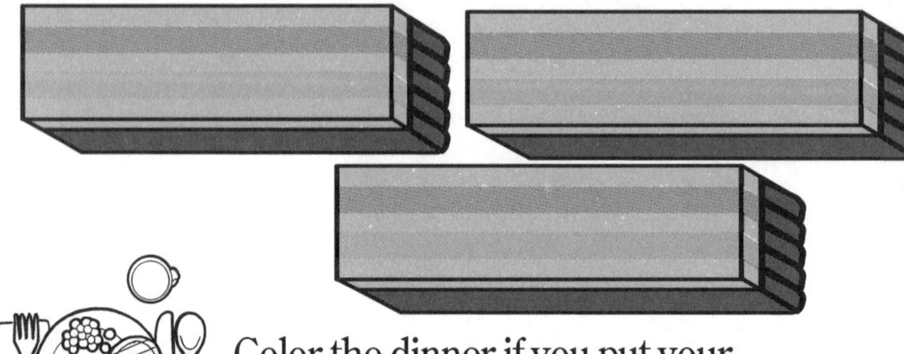

Color the dinner if you put your Home Base Words in the Glossary.

B **Help Needed.** Mrs. Li dropped her card box. Match the syllables to make five list words.

1. ____________________

2. ____________________

3. ____________________

4. ____________________

5. ____________________

C **Riddles.**

1. What word has only four letters? ________________
2. What word is the opposite of before? ________________
3. What word has a, an, no, not, other, he and her in it? ________________
4. What word is the opposite of sister? ________________
5. What word is the opposite of over? ________________
6. What word has each in it? ________________

D **Mixed Order.** Place the letters in the correct order and add an e and r to form list words.

fnig	ohbtr	cateh	nind
________	________	________	________
hoant	twin	stam	ahft
________	________	________	________

E **Through the Year.** These apple trees show the seasons. Write the season below each picture. If you need help check your Word Bank.

__________ __________ __________ __________

Which season is your favorite? ________________

Why? ____

F **Kindly Affectionate.** The Bible says, "Beloved, if God so loved us, we also ought to love one another." (I John 4:11) We are to love one another and be kind and caring. Write about a kind, loving thing you can do for someone.

G Crossed Words. Fill in letters to complete the puzzles.

a

Please give me ____ cookie.

____ the game we got ice cream.

Put on a coat ____ your clothes.

over
after
better
father
water
another
brother
summer
under
teacher
dinner
winter
number
finger
master

f

I cut my ____ on a can.

My ____ went to work.

w

Sometimes it snows in ____.

I need a drink of ____.

u

My ____ is nineteen.

Put your book ____ your chair.

b

My ____ and I went to Sunday School.

You are ____ at basketball than I am.

s

Jesus is our ____.

We go camping in the ____.

r

My ____ is Miss Smith.

We had meat and potatoes for ____.

door
before
more
care
heard
store
dear
floor
story
dinosaur
years
wore
ears
hear
fear

A Pictures and Words.

Write the words with ear on the ear.

Write the words with ore on the store.

Write the words with oor on the door.

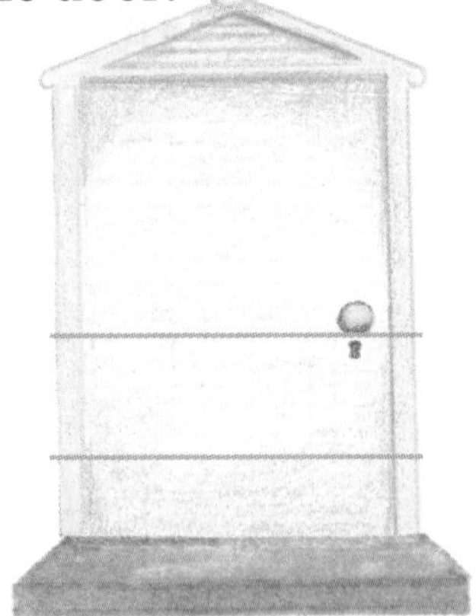

Write the aur word on the dinosaur.

Write the or word on the storybook.

Write the are word on the heart that shows we care.

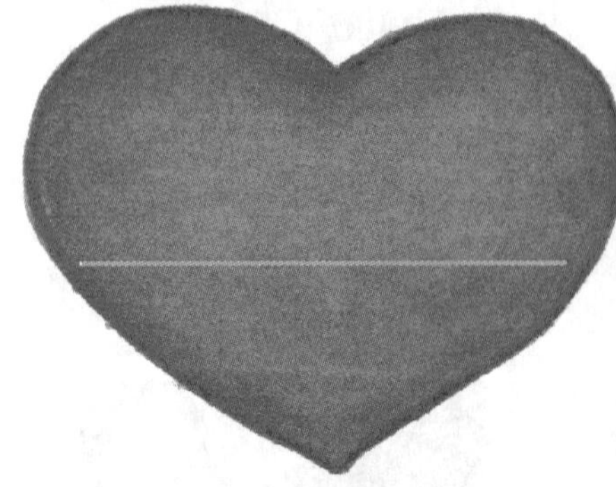

Write your Home Base Words on the dinosaur tracks.

B **Rhymes.** Write in the rhyming words. Remember that the words do not have to be spelled alike.

bear ____________

bird ____________

deer ____________

sore ____________

cheers ____________

C **Robbie Robot.** Robbie's ears are gone. Make him funny new ones.

D **A Letter.** Put in the missing list words.

_______ Grandmother,
I _________ you were
sick _________ Easter.
Do not _______, God
will take _______ of
you. I love you
_______ each day.
Love,

____

E **Word Pictures.** Make two of these words into word pictures. Remember this word picture.

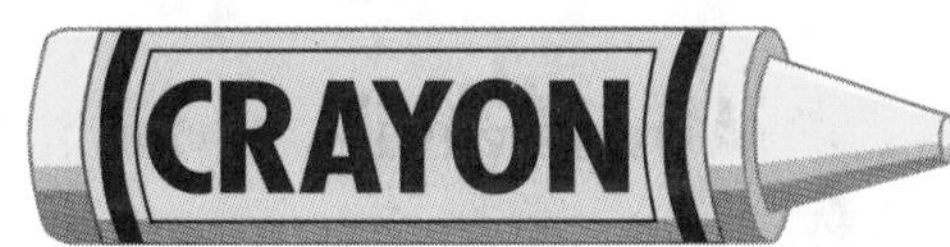

dinosaur floor store heard

F **Future Plans.** The Bible says that God has wonderful plans for us. He wants to help our dreams come true. I Corinthians 2:9 says,

"Eye has not seen, nor ear heard,
Nor have entered into the heart of man
the things which God has prepared for those who love Him."

What do you think God's plans for you are? Write about them.

____

____

____

____

____

____

G **Word Family.** Look at these words; then use them in the sentences.

ear **hear** **heard**

1. Have you ____________ the story about the deaf man?

2. Jesus put His finger in his ____________ and said, "Be opened!"

3. The man said, "I can ____________."

Color the little dinosaur if you put your Home Base Words in the Glossary this week.

Meanings Match. Find the words that fit these meanings.

1. parts of the body to hear with ____________
2. a large animal that lived long ago ____________
3. the opening into a room ____________
4. a building where things are sold ____________
5. to be afraid ____________
6. 365 days, 52 weeks, 12 months ____________

door
before
more
care
heard
store
dear
floor
story
dinosaur
years
wore
ears
hear
fear

Dinosaur Delight. Most people like dinosaurs. Write about a dinosaur and finish the picture below to go with your sentences.

____

____

____

____

different
woman
without
anything
newspaper
yesterday
alike
forever
butterfly
basketball
tomatoes
winner
sunburned
even
happened

A **Spelling News.** Write your list words on the newspaper in the boxes where they belong. Be careful to fit a syllable into each box.

Spelling News

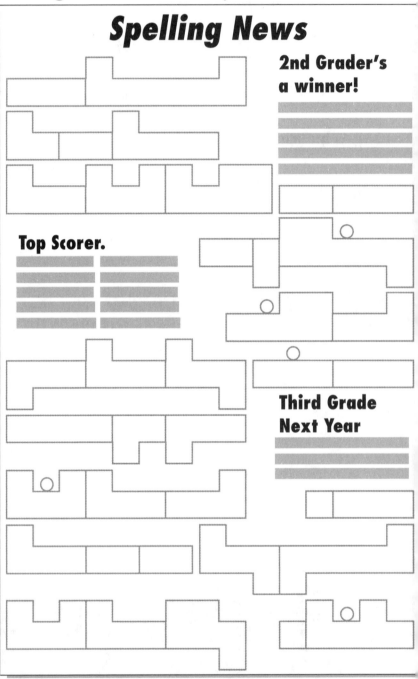

2nd Grader's a winner!

Top Scorer.

Third Grade Next Year

Go back and draw around each syllable in a different colored pencil or crayon.

Color the butterflies if you put your Home Base Words in the Glossary this week.

B **Two in One.** Some of your words this week are compound words. A compound word is two small words put together to make a new word. Put a list word in each sentence.

1. Dad likes to read the ________________ after dinner.
2. We will live with Jesus ________________ in Heaven.
3. The twins look ________________.
4. We saw a ________________ near the flowers.
5. The ________________ team won the game.
6. We got ________________ at the beach when it was hot.
7. I like hamburgers ________________ onions.
8. Do you like ________________ with your hamburger?

C **Match–Ups.** Write the list words that fit these meanings.

1. opposite of alike ________________
2. opposite of man ________________
3. red, round fruits ________________
4. opposite of loser ________________

2 4 6 8
10 12
14

5. opposite of odd ________________
6. something took place ________________
7. the day before today ________________

different
woman
without
anything
newspaper
yesterday
alike
forever
butterfly
basketball
tomatoes
winner
sunburned
even
happened

D **God Is Forever.** *Forever* is a hard word to understand. It means that something never ends. God is forever! He loves us forever! We can live with Him forever! Read Psalm 136:1. Write about why you are glad God's mercy lasts forever.

E **Word Division.** You have two syllable and three syllable words in your list. Write them where they belong and draw a line between the syllables. Check your Glossary for help.

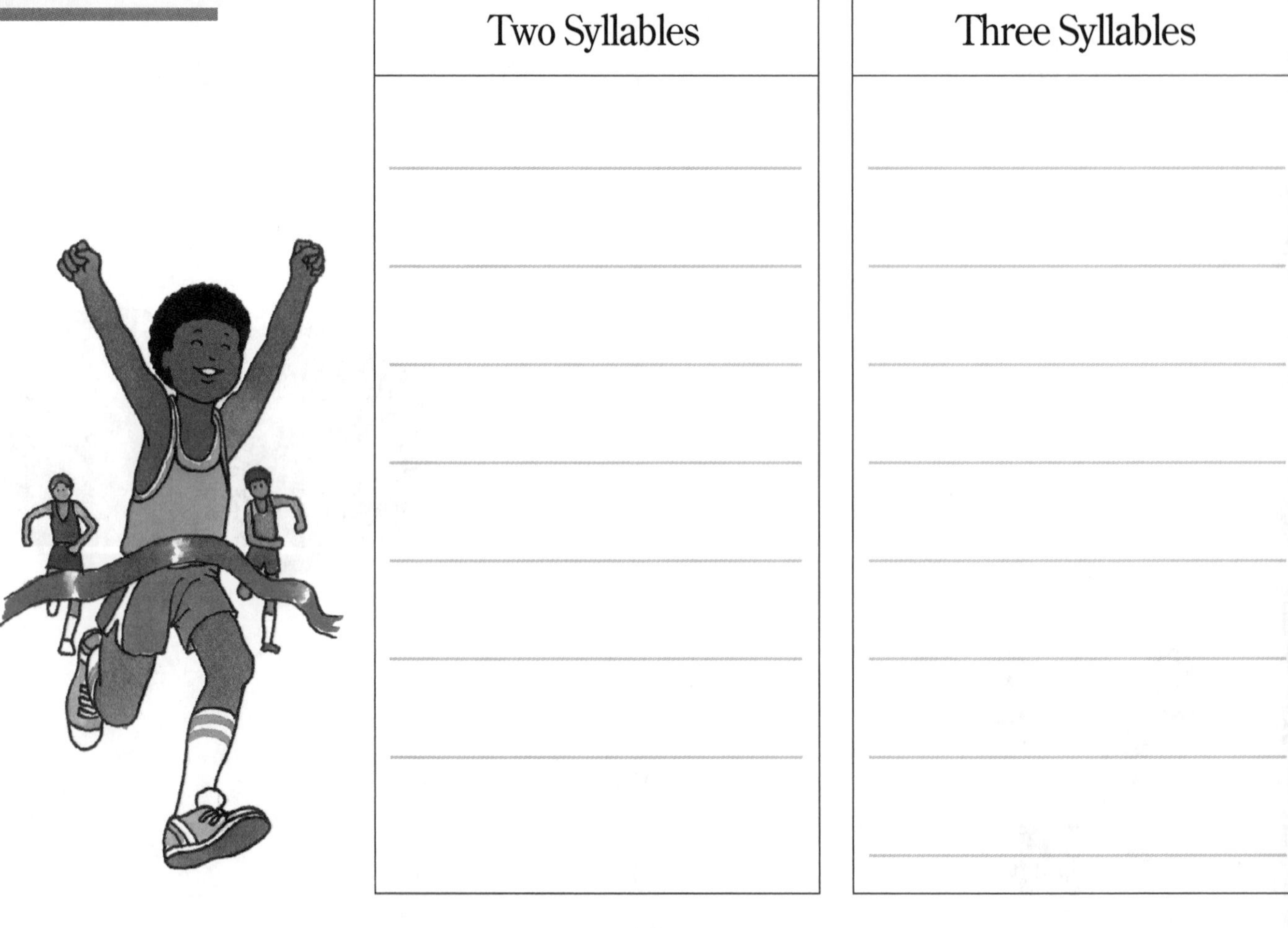

Two Syllables	Three Syllables

F Stories in Code. Use this code to finish these short stories.

A = Z	F = U	K = P	Q = J	V = E
B = Y	G = T	L = O	R = I	W = D
C = X	H = S	M = N	S = H	X = C
D = W	I = R	N = M	T = G	Y = B
E = V	J = Q	O = L	U = F	Z = A
		P = K		

1. __________ (B–V–H–G–V–I–W–Z–B) a __________ (D–L–N–Z–M) planted __________ (G–L–N–Z–G–L–V–H) in her garden. She __________ (S–Z–K–K–V–M–V–W) to see a __________ (Y–F–G–G–V–I–U–O–B). While she worked, she got __________ (H–F–M–Y–F–I–M–V–W).

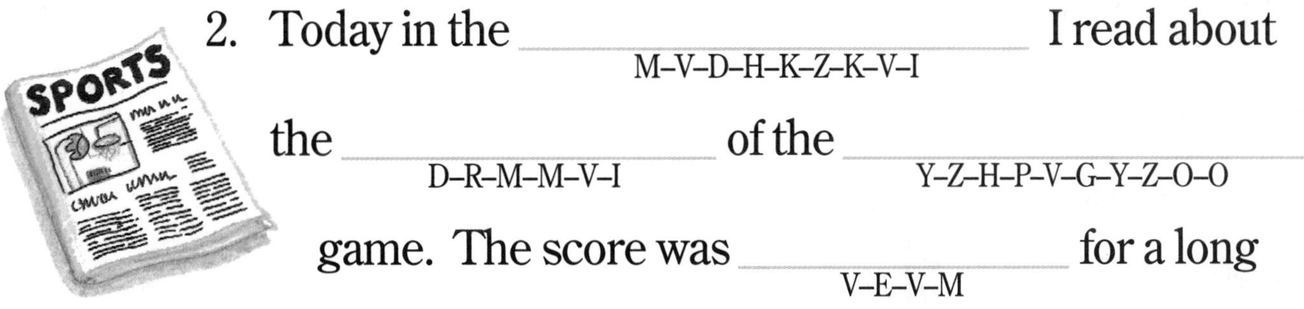

2. Today in the __________ (M–V–D–H–K–Z–K–V–I) I read about the __________ (D–R–M–M–V–I) of the __________ (Y–Z–H–P–V–G–Y–Z–O–O) game. The score was __________ (V–E–V–M) for a long time. Our team played harder and won.

3. Jesus and people are not __________ (Z–O–R–P–V). He was a man but He was __________ (W–R–U–U–V–I–V–M–G). He was __________ (D–R–G–S–L–F–G) sin. He never did __________ (Z–M–B–G–S–R–M–T) wrong. Now He is in Heaven and will live __________ (U–L–I–V–E–V–I).

over
were
after
father
another
brother
morning
heard
anything
Saturday
birthday
summer
March
April
color
before
teacher
different

A **From A to Z.** Put these groups of words in alphabetical order. For some words, you will have to look at the second letter.

before another April March	anything after birthday brother	teacher summer Saturday were

heard color brother different	father different anything birthday	morning March Saturday over

B **Speak Up.** Write the list words that match the glossary markings that tell you how to say a word.

tēch′ ər ____________

bē fôr′ ____________

môrn′ ing ____________

kul′ ər ____________

Match–Ups. Write the list words that match these meanings.

the third month	the fourth month	the day you were born
1. ______	2. ______	3. ______
the warmest season of the year	a person who helps you learn	the last day of the week
4. ______	5. ______	6. ______
the opposite of sister	the opposite of same	the first part of the day
7. ______	8. ______	9. ______

D

Master Teacher. Jesus said that He is our Teacher. In John 13:13 He said, "You call Me Teacher and Lord and you say well, for so I am." Write a list of some things you can learn from Jesus.

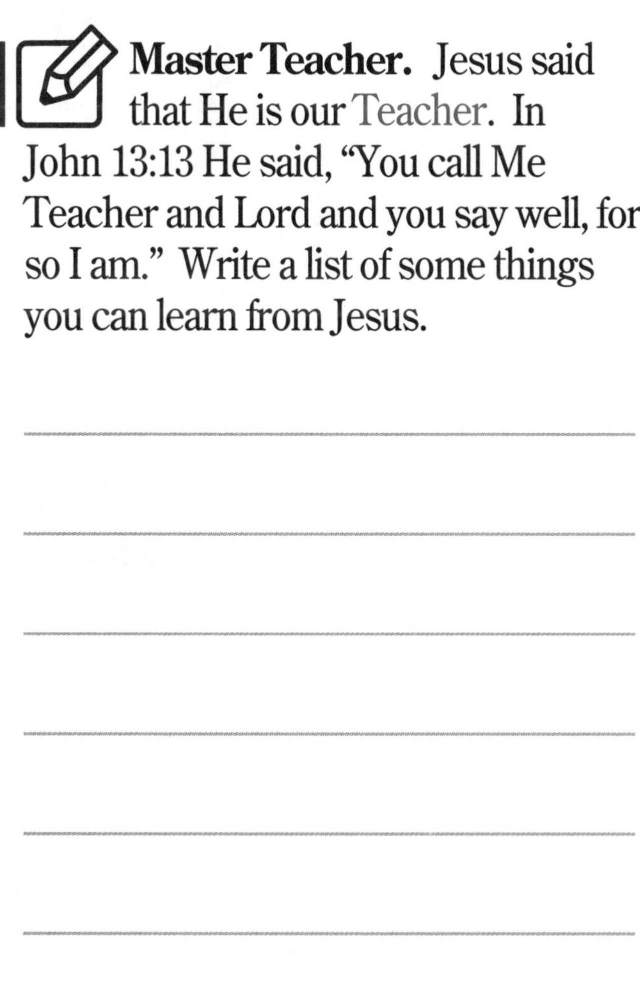

E **Go For Third.** Place a list word with the two other words that are related.

dad, papa, ________________ preacher, coach, ________________

behind, in back, ________________ ahead, in front, ________________

night, noon, ________________ one more, each, ________________

are, was, ________________ March, May, ________________

across, above, ________________ saw, felt, ________________

sister, cousin, ________________ February, April, ________________

fall, spring, ________________ size, shape, ________________

nothing, something, ________________

Friday, Sunday, ________________

cake, presents, ________________

F **Fill–Ins.** Use list words in the sentences where they belong.

1. My ________________ and I bought our dad a card for his birthday.
2. My ________________ at school helped me with my spelling lesson.
3. Bring ________________ you want to eat to the picnic.
4. I will buy ________________ pack of gum for us to share.
5. My ________________ and mother love me very much.

End of the Year. Write a story about this picture. Be sure to use at least five list words in your story.

over
were
after
father
another
brother
morning
heard
anything
Saturday
birthday
summer
March
April
color
before
teacher
different

Billy, Janie, Mike, Beth, Tony, Maria and Robbie Robot have enjoyed the year with you. They hope you have a great vacation and a super year in third grade!

Pronunciation Key for English

Consonants

Sound:	Spelling Examples:
b	baby, bubble, bib
ch	child, much, patch, nature, question, ancient
d	day, ladder, sad, played
f	fish, often, off, phone, cough
g	go, wiggle, big, ghost, league
h	hot, hurry, who
j	jump, age, judge, gym, graduate
k	keep, tickle, sick, cup, picnic, choir, antique
l	look, little, tall
m	my, mommy, come
n	no, winner, nine, know
ng	ring, singing
nk	thank, ankle
p	pie, apple, hope
qu	queen, quiet, (combination of kwh)
r	red, rose
s	see, lesson, miss, city, dance
sh	she, wish, sugar, machine, nation, mission, special
t	tie, tattle, eat, walked
th	think, both, (breath)
th	these, either (voice)
v	vase, save
w	we, well (voice)
wh	what, whether (breath)
y	yes, yellow, onion, million
z	zoo, fuzzy, maze, has
zh	measure, azure, vision

Vowels

Sound:	Spelling Examples:
ā	able, date, aid, day, eight, great
a	apple, hat
ä	father (Same sound as short o)
är	arm, far, sparkle, sorry
ē	me, these, keep, meat, chief, lady, valley, ceiling
e	edge, mess, ready, friend
er	errand, berry, bear, care, arrow, January, fair, heir
ī	I, fine, night, pie, by
i	it, his, gym
ir	miracle, here, ear, deer, superior
īr	fire, retire
ō	open, bone, coat, show, soul
o	top, otter, bother
ô	often, soft, also, haul, caught, draw, bought
oi	oil, joy
oo	book, should
o͞o	cool, tube, stew, fruit, group, to
oor	poor, tour
ȯr	for, more, soar, four, forth, door
ou	out, towel
our	hour, power
ū	use, fuel, pew, Europe, beauty, you
u	fun, couple, another, love (This marking is used in an accented syllable; in an unaccented syllable a schwa is used for the same sound.)
ə	alike, independent, nation, marble
ūr	pure, jury, your
ər	summer, third, turtle, dollar, color, earth, journal (This marking is used in accented or unaccented syllables)

2nd Grade Glossary

Aa

about (ə bout′) *Our class is talking about cows.*

above (ə buv′) to be over something *The moon is above the earth.*

after (af′ tər) when something is finished *Come home after the game.*

alike (ə līk′) the same *The two dolls are alike.*

along (ə lông′) *Bring your sister along when you come.*

and (and) *The boy and girl went down the street.*

ankle (āng′ kəl) part of the leg above the foot *My ankle is sore today.*

another (ə nu′ t̲h̲ər) *John has another friend.*

any (en′ ē) *Are there any crayons in the box?*

anything (en′ ē thing) *You can have anything you want.*

apple (ap′ əl) a fruit *The apple was very good.*

April (ā′ prəl) the fourth month of the year *Her birthday is in April.*

arms (ärmz) upper limbs of the body *He has strong arms.*

around (ə round′) *We walked around the lake.*

as (az) *Are you as hungry as I am?*

asked (askt) *Mom asked me to take out the garbage.*

August (ô′ gəst) the eighth month of the year *We like to have picnics in August.*

aunt (ant, ônt) the sister of your father or mother *My aunt is nice.*

awesome (ô′ səm) very powerful and great *God is awesome.*

awful (ô′ fəl) terrible *That smoke smells awful.*

Bb

baptize (bap′ tīz) *Jesus asked John to baptize Him.*

baseball (bās′ bôl) a game played with a ball and bat *We play baseball at recess.*

basketball (bas′ kət bôl) a ball game *We play basketball at recess.*

because (bi kôz′) *We came to school today because it didn't snow.*

bedroom (bed′ ro͞om) a room for sleeping *The boys shared a bedroom.*

been (ben) *We have been to Disneyland.*

before (bi fôr′) earlier *The mail came before noon.*

began (bi gan′) started *We began to work on our spelling.*

behave (bi hāv′) to act nice *We behave well at school.*

believe (bi lēv′) *I believe in Jesus.*

bell (bel) an object that rings *The church bell is ringing.*

benches (ben′ chəz) seats to sit on *The park benches have been painted.*

better (bet′ ər) *I like your cookies better than mine.*

Bible (bī′ bəl) God's Word *The Bible is God's Word.*

bicycle (bī′ sik əl) a toy to ride on *The green bicycle was the fastest.*

billfold (bil′ fōld) something to keep money in *Mike lost his billfold.*

birthday (bərth′ dā) the day a person was born *When is your birthday?*

blind (blīnd) to not be able to see *The blind girl reads from a special book.*

blue (blo͞o) a color *My blue crayon is broken.*

body (bod′ ē) our flesh *My body is the temple of the Holy Spirit.*

both (bōth) *Both of the bunnies are white.*

break (brāk) *Be careful not to break the glass.*

bright (brīt) very shiny *The sun is bright today.*

bring (bring) *Please bring me another paper.*

brother (bruth′ ər) a boy with the same parents as you *My brother helps me every day.*

brought (brôt) did bring *Marissa brought cupcakes for the class on her birthday.*

brown (broun) a color *I saw a brown horse in the field.*

buckle (buk′ əl) a fastener *The buckle on the pack was broken.*

built (bilt) did build, made *Mary and Becky built a doll house.*

but (but) *I would like to go, but I can't.*

butterfly (but′ ər flī) a flying insect *The butterfly was yellow and black.*

buy (bī) to get something with money *I will buy Mother a present.*

Cc

can't (kant) cannot *I can't help you with that problem.*

candy (kan′ dē) a sweet food *The candy stuck to my teeth.*

care (ker) *We should care for our friends.*

caught (kôt) did catch *Jon caught the dog.*

cheese (chēz) a food made from milk *I like cheddar cheese.*

children (chil′ drən) young people *The children on the playground were having fun.*

chocolate (chok′ lət) a sweet food *Most children like chocolate.*

chosen (chō′ zən) picked *The teacher has chosen his helper.*

Christ (krīst) one of the names of Jesus *Christ died for my sins.*

Christmas (kris′ məs) a holiday to celebrate Jesus' birth *Christmas is lots of fun for our family.*

church (chərch) a special place to worship God *The church service started at 11:00 a.m.*

climbed (klīmd) went up something *The cat climbed over the fence.*

clothes (klōz) things to wear *I got new clothes for Easter.*

coat (kōt) a warm piece of clothing *My new coat is blue.*

cold (kōld) not hot *The ice cream was very cold.*

color (kul′ ər) the tint of something *Jane's favorite color is blue.*

coming (kum′ ing) *Mother is coming home soon.*

cookies (kook′ ēz) a sweet food *I have cookies in my lunch box.*

cost (kôst) price of something *That coat cost $50.00.*

could (kood) was able to *James could ride a horse when he was four.*

cowboys (kou′ boiz) men that work with cows and horses *The cowboys were good at riding horses.*

creation (krē ā′ shən) make something new *The creation of the world took seven days.*

cross (krôs) *Jesus died on the cross.*

cute (kūt) *The baby bunnies are cute.*

Dd

days (dāz) the time of light between morning and evening *There are seven days in a week.*

dear (dir) loved *My mother is dear to me.*

December (di sem′bər) the twelfth month of the year *Christmas is in December.*

different (dif′ ə rənt) not alike *The kittens were different colors.*

dinner (din′ ər) the evening meal *Let's go out for dinner.*

dinosaur (dī′ nə sȯr) large, extinct animal *The dinosaur in the museum is very big.*

dirty (dər′ tē) to have dirt on something *The floor was very dirty.*

doing (do͞o′ ing) *I am doing the dishes tonight.*

don't (dōnt) *We don't have any milk.*

door (dȯr) opening to a room *Open the door to let the breeze in.*

down (doun) not up *Put that heavy box down.*

draw (drô) make a picture *I like to draw horses.*

dream (drēm) *I had a nice dream last night.*

drew (dro͞o) did draw *James drew a picture at school.*

drill (dril) 1. to dig a hole *The man will drill for oil.* 2. a tool used to make holes *Dad used a drill on the wall.*

drink (drink) to swallow some liquid *I would like to drink some milk.*

drive (drīv) to steer a car *Mother had to drive Linda to school.*

Ee

each (ēch) every *We each took two cookies.*

ears (irz) part of the body to hear with *My ears got cold this morning.*

eats (ēts) chews and swallows *My family eats lots of cereal.*

eight (āt) one more than seven *There are eight puppies.*

eve (ēv) the evening or day before a special day *Tonight is Christmas Eve.*

even (ē′ vən) not odd *What are the even numbers?*

every (ev′ rē) each *Every child in the class came to the party.*

eyelids (ī′ lidz) skin that covers the eyes when they are closed *My eyelids are sore.*

Ff

face (fās) the front of the head *My face is dirty.*

faith (fāth) belief or trust *We must have faith in God.*

fall (fôl) 1. a season of the year *School starts in the fall.* 2. to drop *The snow began to fall from the sky.*

father (fä′ t͟hər) male parent *Jim's father is our coach.*

fear (fir) to be afraid *Do you fear snakes?*

February (feb′ ū wer′ ē) the second month of the year *Valentine's Day is in February.*

felt (felt) did feel *Jason felt sick when he got up in the morning.*

finger (fing′ ər) part of the hand *My finger is stiff.*

fire (fīr) something burning *The fire was warm in the stove.*

five (fīv) one more than four *My little brother is five.*

flashlight (flash′ līt) a light with a battery *We need Dad's flashlight.*

flew (flo͞o) did fly *The birds flew to the pond.*

floor (flȯr) the bottom of a room *The floor is sticky.*

flower (flou′ ər) the bloom of a plant *The flower was yellow.*

forever (fȯr′ ev ər) eternity *We will live in Heaven forever.*

forgive (fȯr giv′) to pardon someone for doing you wrong *I forgive you for breaking my toy.*

found (found) did find, not lost *The children found the lost turtle.*

four (fȯr) one less than five *My sister is four years old.*

Friday (frī′ dā) the last day of the school week *On Friday Mrs. Brown will show a film.*

friend (frend) a person you like very much *My best friend is Tara.*

from (frum) not to *I got a package from my friend.*

front (frunt) not back *The front of the book was torn.*

full (fool) not empty *Mother gave me a full glass of water.*

fuss (fus) *The baby began to fuss.*

Gg

games (gāmz) playing with rules *We like to play games at recess.*

garden (gär′ dən) a place to grow plants *We have a big garden this year.*

gave (gāv) did give *My dad gave me a watch for my birthday.*

getting (get′ ing) *Joshua is getting a new puppy.*

giggles (gig′ əlz) small laughs *Marie giggles at the clown.*

girl's (gərlz) belonging to a girl *The girl's brother was looking for her.*

glasses (glas′ əz) 1. something to help you see *My new glasses help me read.* 2. something to drink from *Mom got new tea glasses.*

goes (gōz) *Sally goes to high school.*

going (gō′ ing) *We are going to the store after school.*

good-bye (good′ bī) *Angela said good-bye to her granddad.*

Gospel (gos′ pəl) the teachings of Jesus *Gospel means good news.*

grade (grād) a level in school *Second grade is fun.*

gray (grā) a color *The kitten is gray.*

grow (grō) to get bigger *The plant will grow in the sunshine.*

Hh

happened (hap′ ənd) *The accident happened on our street.*

happy (hap′ ē) to feel good *My mother is happy with me.*

hard (härd) 1. difficult to do *This is hard work in math.* 2. solid *The ice on the pond was hard.*

ıave (hav) *I have a sore finger.*

ıaven't (hav′ ənt) have not *We ıaven't got any milk.*

ıear (hir) *I hear the bells at the ·hurch.*

ıeard (hərd) did hear *We heard he playground bell.*

ıello (hel′ ō) a greeting *Say hello to ·he principal.*

ıere (hir) *Come here and set the ·able, please.*

ıerself (hər self′) *The girl helped ıerself to some cake.*

ıides (hīdz) 1. keeps something a ;ecret *The bird hides her nest in the ·ree.* 2. skins of animals *They used ·he hides to make coats.*

ıigh (hī) not low *Tim threw the ›all high in the air.*

ıike (hīk) walk *We like to hike in ·he woods.*

ıill (hil) a raised part of the earth *It ·s fun to climb a hill.*

ıimself (him self′) *Patrick was ›roud of himself for working so hard.*

Holy (hō′ lē) something about God *The Holy Spirit lives in me.*

horses (hôr′ səz) large animals for riding *The horses were running in the field.*

houses (hou′ səz) buildings that people live in *The houses were all painted white.*

how (hou) *Please tell me how to do this work.*

hung (hung) did hang *Judy hung new curtains in the kitchen.*

hurting (hərt′ ing) feeling badly *Fred's broken toe was really hurting.*

Ii

I'll (īl) I will *I'll get your coat for you.*

if (if) *I will be happy if Granddad comes.*

important (im pôr′ tənt) something that means a lot to you *The Bible is important to me.*

inside (in sīd′) within *Put your coat inside the closet.*

into (in tōō′) *Put the clothes into the basket.*

invite (in vīt′) to ask someone to go somewhere *Who will you invite to your party?*

it's (its) it is or it has *I hope it's okay for you to come to my house.*

Jj

January (jan′ ū wer′ ē) the first month of the year *New Year's Day is in January.*

jaw (jô) the lower part of the face *My jaw was scraped by the swing.*

July (jū lī′) the seventh month *July is a summer month.*

jumped (jumpt) went over something *The horse jumped over the gate.*

June (jūn) the sixth month of the year *June is my favorite month.*

just (just) only *I just need one more book.*

Kk

kitten (kit′ ən) a young cat *The kitten is very sweet.*

knock (nok) *Be sure to knock on the door.*

know (nō) *I know that God loves me.*

Ll

lake (lāk) a body of water with land around it *It's fun to swim in the lake.*

laws (lôz) rules *We must obey all laws.*

leave (lēv) go out *When you are ready to leave, put on your coat.*

left (left) 1. not right *Mother has a ring on her left hand.* 2. did leave *Father left for work.*

legs (legz) the parts of the body used to stand, walk, run and jump *My legs are growing fast.*

life (līf) to be alive *Jesus gives us new life.*

likes (līks) *My puppy likes bones.*

lion (lī′ ən) a large, wild cat *The lion in the zoo is big.*

listen (lis′ ən) to hear something *I like to listen to music.*

little (lit′ əl) small *The little dog was lost.*

Lord (lȯrd) one of God's names *Jesus is Lord of all the earth.*

lunchroom (lunch′ rōōm) a room to eat lunch in *The lunchroom was crowded.*

Mm

many (men′ ē) a lot *There were many marbles in the bag.*

March (märch) third month of the year *My dad's birthday is in March.*

master (mas′ tər) the leader *The Lord is my Master.*

meat (mēt) part of an animal used for food *We got meat for dinner at the store.*

mess (mes) *Clean up the mess in your room.*

met (met) did meet *We met our grandfather at church.*

middle (mid′ əl) center *The middle of the room was empty.*

might (mīt) maybe *We might go on vacation this summer.*

mild (mīld) soft, gentle *My family likes mild taco sauce.*

milk (milk) a drink that comes from cows *We always have milk for breakfast.*

mind (mīnd) 1. obey *The teacher wants us to mind her.* 2. your brain *You have a good mind.*

miracle (mir′ ə kəl) something only God can do *When Jesus calmed the storm, it was a miracle.*

mix-up (miks′ up) *There was a mix-up with our order.*

Monday (mun′ dā) the second day of the week *School will start Monday.*

money (mun′ ē) paper and coins used to buy things *Monica had money for the telephone call.*

more (mȯr) *Mother put more clothes in the wash.*

morning (mȯrn′ ing) the first part of the day *I got up at 7:00 this morning.*

mouse (mous) a small, furry animal *The mouse lived in a hole in the wall.*

mouth (mouth) part of the head used for eating *Sara had her mouth full of oatmeal.*

move (m o͞o v) *My family will move to Texas.*

music (mū′ zik) a song *I like the music at church.*

myself (mī self′) *I can do the math problem myself.*

Nn

need (nēd) *I need some help with my homework.*

newspaper (nōōz′ pā′ pər) a paper that prints news *The newspaper told about the flood.*

nineteen (nīn tēn′) the number before twenty *There were nineteen students in the class.*

north (nȯrth) a direction *The highway to the north is closed.*

nose (nōz) the part of the face used for breathing and smelling *The cold air made her nose red.*

nothing (nuth′ ing) *There is nothing in the box.*

November (nō vem′ bər) the eleventh month of the year *We celebrate Thanksgiving in November.*

now (nou) *It is now time to study.*

number (num′ bər) a way to count things *The number of marbles in the jar is eight.*

Oo

October (ok tō′ bər) the tenth month of the year *My birthday is in October.*

of (uv) *I want one of the kittens.*

off (ôf) not on *The flowers fell off the table.*

one (wun) one less than two *There is one dog in the yard.*

only (ōn′ lē) *There is only one paper left in the notebook.*

open (ō′ pən) not closed *The door to the oven was open.*

orange (ȯr′ ənj) 1. a color *The orange flowers are beautiful.* 2. fruit *I had an orange in my lunch.*

our (our) belonging to us *That is our rabbit.*

out (out) not in *Put the cats out before you leave.*

over (ō′ vər) above, across *The deer jumped over the fence.*

Pp

packs (paks) *Tina packs a suitcase when she goes to camp.*

pages (pā′ jəz) sheets of paper in a book *There are ten pages in the book.*

paid (pād) past of pay *We paid three dollars for the book.*

parking (pär′ king) places to put cars *There is plenty of parking space at the shopping center.*

party (pär′ tē) when people get together to have fun or to celebrate *The party is at 7:00 tonight.*

peace (pēs) freedom from fighting *Jesus gives us peace.*

pencil (pen′ səl) a tool for writing or drawing *A sharp pencil writes neatly.*

people (pē′ pəl) human beings *God loves all the people in the world.*

picnic (pik′ nik) a trip with food taken along *We had watermelon on the picnic.*

pie (pī) a dessert *Sue likes apple pie.*

piece (pēs) a part of something *I would like a piece of pie.*

pink (pink) a color *Her new blouse was pink.*

pizza (pēt′ sə) a flat crust topped with cheese, tomato sauce and other foods *The pizza tastes good.*

plants (plants) *We have lettuce plants in our garden.*

played (plād) *After school Jenny played with her dolls.*

please (plēz) *It is polite to say, "Please."*

poor (poor) *The poor cat got all wet.*

praise (prāz) to worship *Praise is thanking God for something.*

pretty (prit′ ē) lovely *The flowers are pretty.*

price (prīs) the cost of something *The price of the bike is $100.00.*

print (print) to write something *The teacher will print our spelling words.*

puddle (pud′ əl) a small bit of water *The puddle was in the middle of the street.*

pull (pool) not push *The horse can pull a wagon.*

puppy (pup′ ē) a baby dog *The puppy was very hungry.*

purple (pər′ pəl) a color *The purple robe looked good on the king.*

pushing (poosh′ ing) *The teacher is pushing the swing.*

puzzles (puz′ əlz) games with pieces to put together *The puzzles were hard.*

Qq

quick (quik) fast *Be quick to get your work done.*

Rr

rabbit (rab′ ət) a small furry animal with long ears *The rabbit is white.*

reading (rēd′ ing) to read something *I like reading my book.*

really (ril′ ē) *My mother really liked the present.*

repent (ri pent′) to be sorry and change *We should repent if we lie.*

rested (rest′ əd) *We rested after our late night.*

right (rīt) 1. not left *The new mitt fits Jason's right hand.* 2. not wrong *Your answer is right.*

roadway (rōd′ wā) a street for cars to drive on *The roadway was crowded.*

rocket (rok′ ət) *The rocket was powerful.*

roll (rōl) 1. to push something to another person *Roll the ball to me.* 2. a piece of baked bread *That roll tasted great.*

ropes (rōps) strong cords *The box had ropes around it.*

roses (rōz′ əz) sweet-smelling flowers *Dad gave Mother some red roses.*

rules (ro͞ols) *The rules of our school help us.*

Ss

sad (sad) not happy *The story was sad.*

safe (sāf) *Your dog is safe with me.*

said (sed) did say, spoke *The teacher said that it was time to go home.*

sailboat (sāl′ bōt) a boat with a sail *The sailboat went quickly across the lake.*

salt (sôlt) a seasoning for food *Please pass the salt.*

salvation (sal vā′ shən) *Salvation comes only from Jesus.*

sang (sāng) did sing, made music with voices *We sang songs in chapel.*

Saturday (sat′ ər dā) the seventh day of the week *On Saturday we are going to the park.*

Savior (sāv′ yər) a person who saves *Jesus is the Savior of the world.*

saw (sô) 1. a tool *The saw was on the workbench.* 2. did see *We saw a whale in the ocean.*

saying (sā′ ing) speaking *The class was saying Psalm 23.*

schools (sko͞olz) places to get an education *Teams from many schools came to the game.*

science (sī′ əns) *Science is Michael's favorite subject.*

seen (sēn) *The tiger was seen in the jungle.*

September (sep tem′ bər) the ninth month of the year *School often begins in September.*

set (set) put down *I set my glass on the table.*

seven (sev′ ən) one more than six *There were seven people in the car.*

shall (shal) will *What shall we do with our papers?*

sheet (shēt) one piece of something *Mary gave Nancy a sheet of paper.*

she's (shēz) she is or she has *She's our new art teacher.*

shoelace (sho͞o′ lās) *The shoelace on my tennis shoe broke.*

shoes (sho͞oz) *I like your new shoes.*

should (shood) must *You should help your parents when you can.*

simple (sim′ pəl) easy, not difficult *The workbook page was simple.*

six (siks) one more than five *Here are six marbles.*

slides (slīdz) 1. to move smoothly *The skater slides over the ice.* 2. playground equipment *We played on the slides.*

slow (slō) not fast *We were very slow at doing our work.*

snakes (snāks) *I saw snakes at the zoo.*

snow (snō) frozen rain *There is snow on the mountains.*

soft (sôft) not hard *The pillow was very soft.*

some (sum) *Let me give you some help.*

something (sum′ thing) *I have to get something for Dad's birthday.*

sometimes (sum′ tīmz) once in a while *Sometimes I feel sad.*

soon (sōōn) in a short time *You need to clean up your room soon.*

sorry (sär′ ē) *Nathan was sorry for hurting Brandon's feelings.*

south (south) a direction *New York is south of Maine.*

speak (spēk) to say something *I have to speak to my class.*

special (spesh′ əl) *Frank has a special stuffed animal.*

spend (spend) to buy something with money *Don't spend all your allowance today.*

Spirit (spir′ ət) *God sent the Spirit to live with His people.*

spring (spring) 1. a season of the year *In the spring we get out of school.* 2. a coiled wire *I lost the spring for my ball point pen.*

start (stärt) to begin *Please start the race soon.*

stayed (stād) *We stayed with Aunt Sue while Mom was gone.*

sticker (stik′ ər) a stamp *The principal gave us each a sticker.*

still (stil) *We still want a puppy.*

stood (stood) did stand, not sat *The whole class stood to say the flag salute.*

store (stȯr) a building to buy things *The store closes soon.*

story (stȯr′ ē) *The story about the dinosaur was great.*

strong (strông) to be powerful *The strong man lifted the big box.*

such (such) *The monkeys at the zoo made such loud noises.*

summer (sum′ ər) the warmest season of the year *In the summer we like to swim.*

sunburned (sun′ bərnd) had the skin burned by the sun *Patsy had sunburned arms.*

Sunday (sun′ dā) the first day of the week *On Sunday we go to church.*

surprise (sər prīz′) *Dad had a surprise for me in his pocket.*

swim (swim) to move in the water *It is fun to swim in the summer.*

swing (swing) playground equipment *The new swing is lots of fun for the children.*

Tt

ake (tāk) *Be sure to take your coat o school.*

eacher (tē′ chər) a person who eaches others *I like my teacher.*

eam (tēm) a group that plays ogether *Our team won the soccer ame.*

eeth (tēth) hard parts of the mouth ısed for chewing and biting *The lentist will look at Anne's teeth.*

elephone (tel′ ə fōn) a machine ısed to call people *My grandma got ı new telephone.*

en (ten) one more than nine *My ister is ten years old.*

hank you (thānk′ ū) *Thank you for he new doll.*

hat (that) *I am happy that you are ıere.*

hen (then) *Eat your supper and hen have dessert.*

here (ther) *There are ten teachers n the school.*

hese (thēz) *I like these shoes.*

hey (thā) *They came to our house o fix the roof.*

thick (thik) not thin *We ate thick slices of bread.*

thinking (think′ ing) *I was thinking about lunch during the test.*

third (thərd) *Third grade will be fun.*

this (this) *This is your job for today.*

those (thōz) *Those books belong to the teacher.*

thought (thôt) did think *We thought we saw a hummingbird.*

three (thrē) one less than four *There are three roses on the bush.*

thumb (thum) a part of the hand *My thumb got caught in the door.*

Thursday (thərz′ dā) the fifth day of the week *Tomorrow is Thursday.*

tickets (tik′ əts) a paper that lets you attend something *We had two tickets to the circus.*

tickles (tik′ əlz) makes a person laugh *The little tickles felt good.*

tired (tīrd) *I feel tired after school.*

today (tə dā′) the present time *Today is Wednesday.*

tomatoes (tə mā′ tōz) round red fruit *The tomatoes were juicy.*

too (to͞o) also *I like pizza, too.*

towel (tou′ əl) a cloth to dry with *The new towel was blue.*

track (trak) a path or race course *The runners ran around the track.*

truck (truk) *The truck had big logs on it.*

true (tro͞o) not false *Your answer is true.*

truth (tro͞oth) *Always tell the truth.*

try (trī) *She will try to do her best.*

Tuesday (to͞oz′ dā) the third day of the week *Tomorrow is Tuesday.*

turn (tərn) to change direction *Please turn around and go to your seat.*

two (to͞o) one more than one *There were two children on the slide.*

Uu

uncle's (unk′ əlz) belonging to an uncle *My uncle's name is Ted.*

under (un′ dər) below *Put a napkin under your plate.*

until (un til′) *It is one hour until bedtime.*

used (ūzd) *We used all the soap in the kitchen.*

Vv

verse (vərs) a part of a song or Bible section *The third verse will be sung by the choir.*

very (ver′ ē) *We were very tired after the race.*

vine (vīn) long, thin stem of a plant *There are lots of grapes on the vine.*

Ww

wagon (wag′ ən) a four wheeled cart *Bill put wood in the wagon.*

walked (wôkt) *The boys walked to the store after school.*

wants (wônts) *Mary wants a piece of pie.*

washes (wôsh′ əz) makes clean *Mother washes the dishes.*

water (wôt′ ər) *We get a drink of water after recess.*

Wednesday (wenz′ dā) the fourth day of the week *Wednesday is a vacation day.*

weekend (wēk′ end) Saturday and Sunday *What are you doing this weekend?*

went (went) did go *We went to church on Sunday.*

were (wər) past of are *We were first in the contest.*

what (whät) *What are you doing after school?*

when (when) *When is your mother coming home?*

where (wher) *Where did you put my book?*

which (which) *Which one of these dresses do you like?*

while (whīl) during the time *Let's play while the cookies bake.*

white (whīt) the lightest color *The white horse ran the fastest.*

why (whī) *Why are you working so hard?*

win (win) *It is fun to win games.*

winner (win′ ər) one who wins *The winner of the race was Mike.*

winter (win′ tər) the coldest season of the year *In the winter we like to ski.*

wisdom (wiz′ dəm) to know what is right *Jesus gives us wisdom.*

wise (wīz) *God wants us to be wise.*

wishes (wish′ əz) wants *He made two wishes and blew out the candles.*

with (with) together *Can you go with me to the store?*

without (with′ out) not having something *Tara came without her lunch money.*

woman (woom′ən) female *The first woman was Eve.*

word (wərd) *I wrote a word on the board.*

wore (wȯr) *The tall man wore a hat.*

working (wərk′ ing) trying hard on a job *The men are working on the playground.*

worship (wər′ ship) *We worship God in chapel.*

would (wood) *I would like to go to the park.*

write (rīt) *I need to write to my grandmother.*

Yy

years (yirz) *My sister is three years old.*

yellow (yel′ ō) a color *The paper for art is yellow.*

yesterday (yes′ tər dā) the day before today *Yesterday we went to the zoo.*

yoke (yōk) a wooden harness used to hook work animals together *The farmer used a yoke on the oxen.*

yours (yoorz) belonging to you *That lunchbox is yours.*

Zz

zero (zē′ rō) nothing *My answer to number two is zero.*

2nd Grade Word Bank

Home Base and Personal Words

Aa

a
about
above
add
after
airplane
alike
all
along
am
and
ankle
another
any
anything
apple
April
are
arms
around
as
asked
at
ate
August
aunt
away
awesome
awful

Bb

baby
back
ball
baptize
baseball
basketball
be
because
bed
bedroom
beehive
been
before
began
behave
believe
bell
benches
better
Bible
bicycle
big
bike
billfold
birthday
bite
black
bless
blind
blue
body
books
both
box
boy
break
bright
bring
brother
brought
brown
buckle
bug
built
but
butterfly
buy

Home Base and Personal Words

Cc

cake
calling
came
can
can't
candy
car
care
cat
caught
check
cheese
child
children
chips
chocolate
chosen
Christ
Christmas
church
class
climbed
clock
close
clothes
coat
cold
color
come
coming
cookies
cost
could
cowboys
creation
crops
cross
cut
cute

Dd

day
days
dear
December
did
different
dinner
dinosaur
dirty
dive
do
dog
doing
dolls
don't
done
door
down
draw
dream
dress
drew
drill
drink
drive
dry
duck

Ee

each
ears
eats
eggs
eight
end
Eve
eve
even
every
eyelids

Home Base and Personal Words

Ff

face
faith
fall
fast
father
fear
February
feel
feet
felt
finding
fine
finger
fire
first
fish
five
fix
flags
flashlight
flew
floor
flower
fly
food
for
forever
forgive
found
four
Friday
friend
from
front
full
fun
fuss

Gg

games
garden
gave
get
getting
giggles
girl
girl's
give
glad
glasses
go
God
goes
going
gone
good
good-bye
Gospel
got
grade
gray
green
grow

Home Base and Personal Words

Hh

had
hall
hand
hanging
happened
happy
hard
has
have
haven't
hear
heard
hello
here
herself
hides
high
hike
hill
him
himself
Holy
home
hope
horses
houses
how
hung
hurting

Ii

I
I'll
I'm
if
important
in
inside
into
invite
is
it
it's

Jj

January
jaw
Jesus
July
jumped
June
just

Kk

keep
kick
kind
king
kiss
kitten
knock
know

Home Base and Personal Words

Ll

lake
last
late
laws
leave
left
legs
let
life
like
likes
lion
listen
little
live
long
look
Lord
lost
love
lunchroom

Mm

made
mall
man
many
March
master
me
meat
meeting
men
mess
met
middle
might
mild
milk
mind
miracle
miss
mix-up
mom
Monday
money
more
morning
mother
mouse
mouth
move
Mr.
Mrs.
much
mud
music
must
my
myself

Nn

name
neck
need
new
newspaper
nice
nine
nineteen
no
noon
north
nose
not
note
nothing
November
now
number

Home Base and Personal Words

Oo

October
of
off
old
on
one
only
open
orange
our
out
over

Pp

packs
pages
paid
paper
parking
party
peace
pencil
people
pet
pick
picnic
pie
piece
pink
pizza
plants
plate
play
played
please
poor
praise
pray
pretty
price
print
prize
puddle
pull
puppy
purple
push
pushing
put
puzzles

Qq Rr

quick
rabbit
ran
reading
really
red
repent
rested
ride
right
ringing
rink
rip
roadway
rock
rocket
rode
roll
ropes
roses
rules
run

Ss

sad
safe
said
sailboat
salt
salvation
sang
Saturday
save
Savior
saw
saying
school
schools
science
see
seed
seen
sent
September
set
seven
shall
shape
she
she's
sheet
shell
shoelace
shoes
shop
should
show
sick
side
simple
sing
sink
six
skate
sky
sleep
slide
slides
slow
small
smile
snack
snakes
snow
so
socks
soft
some
something
sometimes
soon
sorry
south
space
speak
special
spell
spend
Spirit
spot
spring
star
start
stayed
sticker
still
stood
stop
store
story
strong
such
summer
sun
sunburned
Sunday
surprise
swim
swing

Home Base and Personal Words

Tt

take
talking
tall
teacher
team
teeth
telephone
tell
ten
thank you
that
the
then
there
these
they
thick
thing
think
thinking
third
this
those
thought
three
thumb
Thursday
tickets
tickles
time
tired
to
today
toe
told
tomatoes
too
took
top
towel
track
trees
truck
true
trust
truth
try
Tuesday
turn
two

Uu

uncle's
under
until
up
us
used

Vv

verse
very
vine

Home Base and Personal Words

Ww

wagon
walk
walked
wall
want
wants
was
washes
water
we
Wednesday
week
weekend
well
went
were
what
when
where
which
while
white
who
why
will
win
wink
winner
winter
wisdom
wise
wish
wishes
with
without
woman
word
wore
working
worship
would
write

Xx Yy Zz

years
yellow
yes
yesterday
yoke
you
your
yours
zero
zoo